The
RAILWAY AGE

1855 TO 1880

Published by The Reader's Digest Association Inc.
London • New York • Sydney • Montreal

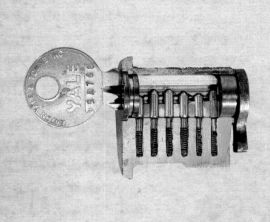

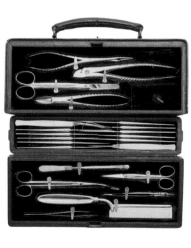

Contents

Introduction

The seething ferment of change and extraordinary dynamism of the Industrial Revolution settled into a phase of consolidation and rationalisation in the later 19th century. The Victorian era of empire in Great Britain, the Second Empire in France, the reign of Tsar Alexander II in Russia, Italian unification and the rise of Germany to nationhood all brought to the fore a new generation intent on progress and modernisation. At the same time, two new powers emerged to challenge the status quo of European dominance: the United States of America, resurgent after the carnage of the American Civil War, and Japan under the Meiji Restoration that saw the end of the Tokugawa shoguns.

The new world order was one of increasingly large power blocs comprising nation states, colonial empires and zones of influence. This in turn encouraged the development of efficient transport networks to traverse these vast territories. Huge civil engineering projects like the Suez Canal and the American transcontinental railroad cut swathes across the narrowly drawn

Imperial link *The Suez Canal cuts through the sands of the Egyptian desert, linking the Mediterranean and Red seas. Built as a French-Egyptian project, it opened in 1869, cutting months off the journey time from Britain to India.*

boundaries of former times. Improved transport and communication combined with free trade to spread technological advances into the remotest regions of the Earth. This was the era in which the modern global market economy was born. It also saw the dawn of the machine age, with mechanisation set to increase still further with electricity and the motor car looming on the horizon.

Inevitably, scientific and social developments brought profound change to people's lives. The exodus from the countryside to the town, which had begun in the early 1800s, continued to gather pace. Major new conurbations sprang up around mining, iron and steel centres, and also around the new petrochemical industries: the Ruhr in Germany, the Sheffield area in England, the coal and steel belt of northern France and southern Belgium. Cities just kept on growing: from a population of around 1 million in 1800, London mushroomed to 4.5 million by 1880. Meanwhile Paris, completely rebuilt by Baron Haussmann, doubled in size. This rampant urbanisation harboured serious threats to both public health and public order.

The editors

▲ In 1856 Neanderthal Man emerged from the mists of time when fossil remains dating back 40,000 years were discovered in the Neander Valley in Germany

► A silk dress made in 1862 and dyed with mauveine, the world's first artificial (aniline) dye patented by William Henry Perkin in 1856

▲ The Bessemer converter, invented in 1855, revolutionised the process of transforming cast iron to steel; by the late 19th century steel was widely used throughout all branches of heavy industry

Towards the end of the 19th century the internal combustion engine – invented in the 1860s by the Belgian engineer Étienne Lenoir – became the driving force behind a new revolution in power and mobility. More efficient methods of extracting and

► In 1859 Edwin Drake's oil-drilling operation in Pennsylvania, USA, started pumping up thousands of barrels of oil, prompting a rush by prospectors to exploit this new energy source; before long, the business of oil extraction was transformed from a small-scale cottage industry to a multi-billion dollar global operation

◄ An image from Wolfgang Staudte's 1951 film *Man of Straw* recalls the introduction of toilet paper to the upper classes; there was a growing awareness of hygiene in the second half of the 19th century and toilet paper – invented by the American Joseph Cayetty in 1857 – began to be manufactured in rolls from 1879 onwards

processing oil made it possible to produce a plentiful supply of petrol, leading to the development of lighter, smaller engines. Before long, these new engines would become the power source of choice in workshops and vehicles, foreshadowing the demise

▼ In 1862 the first naval engagement between ironclad warships, the USS *Monitor* and the CSS *Virginia*, took place at Hampton Roads during the American Civil War

◄ In 1859 the English naturalist Charles Darwin published *On the Origin of Species by Natural Selection*, a seminal work that laid the foundations of the theory of evolution

▲ This early motor car – one of the first petrol-driven cars ever built – was made in 1895 by the British engineer John Henry Knight, combining the principle of the internal combustion engine (devised by Étienne Lenoir) with the new energy source provided by gasoline

of steam. But for now steam still ruled, with steam-powered railways criss-crossing Europe and America, linking cities great and small. The development of urban rail transport – underground in London, elevated in New York – began to ease the growing

▲ Railway development took a significant step forward in 1866, when construction began on the first American transcontinental railroad

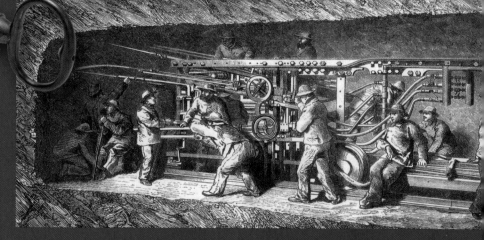

▲ Joseph Bramah's cylinder lock of 1784, an important stage in the development of the modern security lock

► The pneumatic drill designed and built by French engineer Germain Sommelier and first put to work in 1861 on the task it was invented for: boring the Mont Cenis railway tunnel through the Alps

congestion on city streets. On the oceans, steam was just getting into its stride as steamships increasingly replaced sail, reducing journey times. The world shrank further with the construction of the Suez Canal, taking months off the voyage from Britain to India.

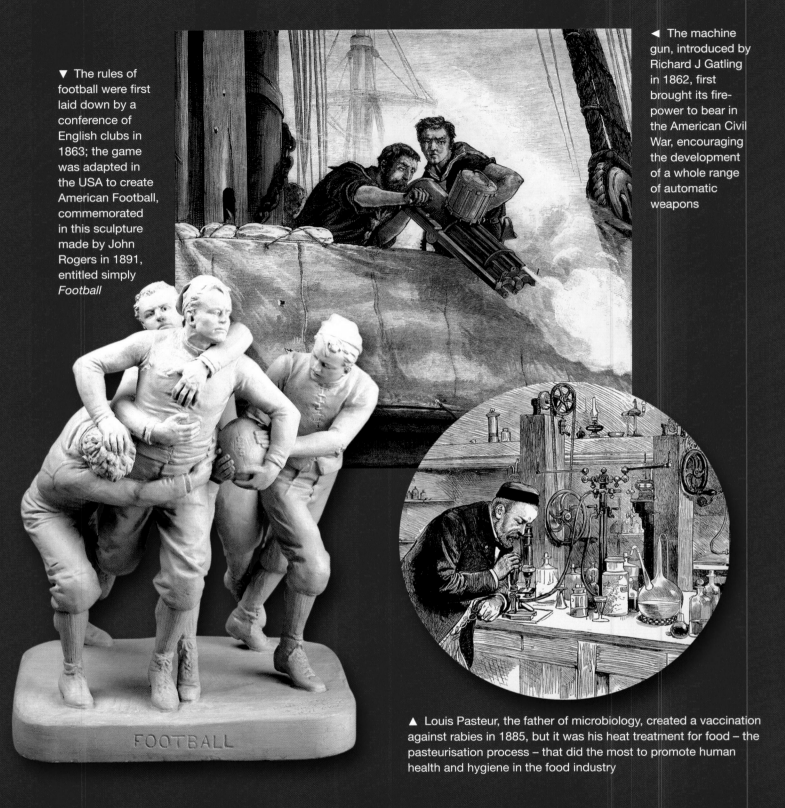

▼ The rules of football were first laid down by a conference of English clubs in 1863; the game was adapted in the USA to create American Football, commemorated in this sculpture made by John Rogers in 1891, entitled simply *Football*

FOOTBALL

◄ The machine gun, introduced by Richard J Gatling in 1862, first brought its fire-power to bear in the American Civil War, encouraging the development of a whole range of automatic weapons

▲ Louis Pasteur, the father of microbiology, created a vaccination against rabies in 1885, but it was his heat treatment for food – the pasteurisation process – that did the most to promote human health and hygiene in the food industry

Coal was king, fuelling not just steamships and trains but also providing – in conjunction with iron thanks to a process invented by Henry Bessemer – the basis for the growth of the steel industry. This in turn led to stronger rails for the railways, armour-plating on

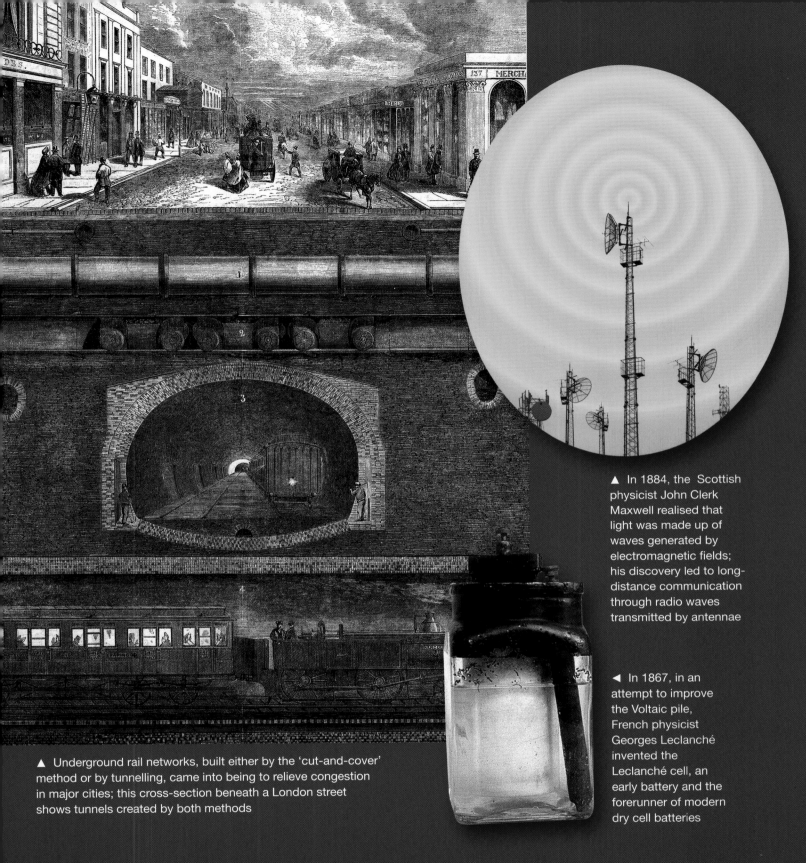

▲ In 1884, the Scottish physicist John Clerk Maxwell realised that light was made up of waves generated by electromagnetic fields; his discovery led to long-distance communication through radio waves transmitted by antennae

◄ In 1867, in an attempt to improve the Voltaic pile, French physicist Georges Leclanché invented the Leclanché cell, an early battery and the forerunner of modern dry cell batteries

▲ Underground rail networks, built either by the 'cut-and-cover' method or by tunnelling, came into being to relieve congestion in major cities; this cross-section beneath a London street shows tunnels created by both methods

battleships, girders and internal structures in buildings, as steel was put to myriad uses. While the 19th century strode confidently into the future, it also produced major contributions to our understanding of the past. Charles Darwin's theory of evolution,

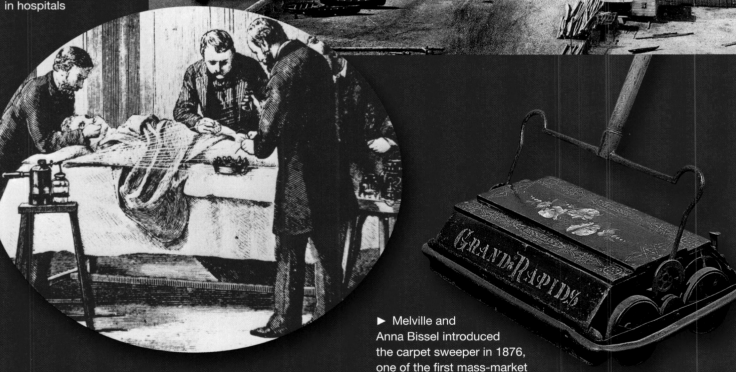

► One of the most awesome civil engineering feats of the entire 19th century was the digging of the Suez Canal, a ten-year project (1859–69) masterminded by Ferdinand de Lesseps

▼ The work of Louis Pasteur and Joseph Lister – the English surgeon who in 1865 was the first to use antiseptics in an operation – led to the introduction of asepsis and antiseptics as standard procedure in hospitals

► Melville and Anna Bissel introduced the carpet sweeper in 1876, one of the first mass-market domestic appliances

the discovery of Neanderthal man, the archaeological excavation of the ancient city of Troy – all transformed the accepted view of history. Other scientists worked to improve conditions in the here and now. Louis Pasteur, through the invention of pasteurisation,

► Barbed wire first appeared in the USA in 1867, as a way for homesteaders to coral their cattle and keep their crops safe from roaming animals

▲ Zenobe Gramme's dynamo, a self-exciting DC generator which he demonstrated to the French Academy of Sciences in 1871, heralded the beginning of the end for the steam engine

Moins Chère que le Beurre!

VÉGÉTALINE

LA VÉGÉTALINE

IMP. MARSEILLAISE - MARSEILLE

▲ In 1869 Napoleon III of France launched a competition to find a butter substitute that would cost less and keep better; the winner, margarine, found a ready market in poorer households

and Joseph Lister, through the use of antiseptics in operations and hospital practice, have saved countless lives. At the time, they also contributed to an all-pervading belief that technological progress would steadily improve people's lot. Outward symbols of the

▼ The invention, in 1857, of a refrigeration machine based on the compression of ammonia gas was the first step towards the introduction of refrigerators in homes, like this one from the 1920s

▲ German archaeologist Heinrich Schliemann's excavation of the ancient city of Troy in the 1870s brought to light many priceless artefacts, such as this golden pin (shown here in a replica of the original) from the hoard that he called 'Priam's Treasure'

▲ International expositions became hugely popular in the second half of the 19th century, beginning with the Great Exhibition held in London's Hyde Park in 1851; this image (above) is of the Paris exhibition of 1900, which attracted more than 50 million visitors

► In the late 19th century the typewriter was the ultimate in new business machines; this model was made in 1897 by Underwood, one of the leading early manufacturers

Victorian faith in the future were the great universal expositions, which acted both as a showcase for technological innovation and a spur to more creativity. The latest discoveries unveiled at these fairs boosted the prestige of individual nations, yet also testified to

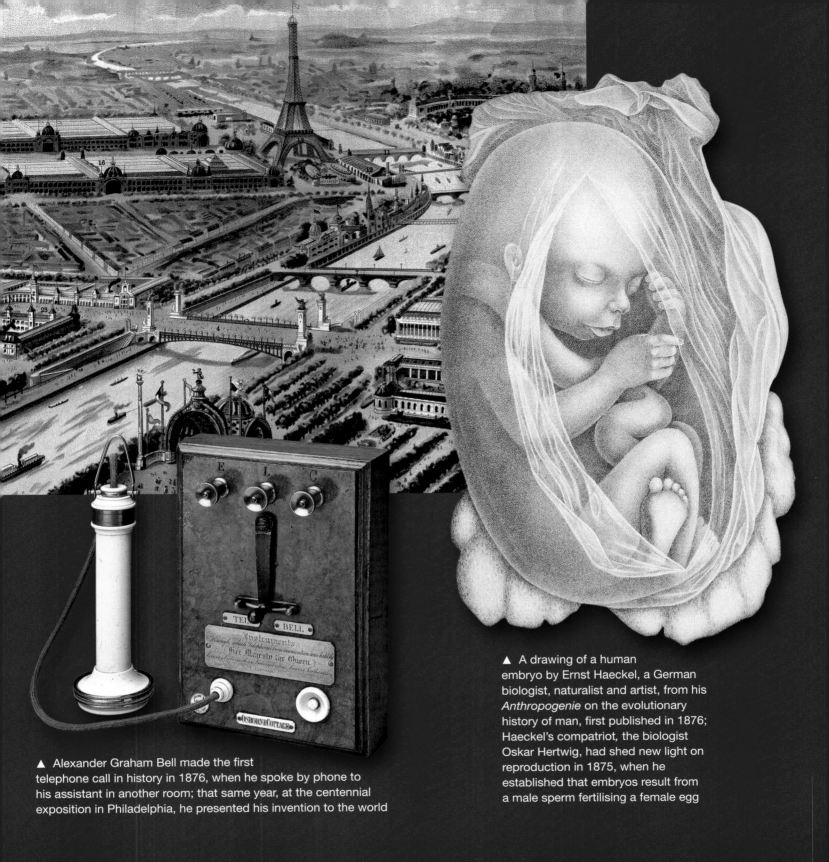

▲ Alexander Graham Bell made the first
telephone call in history in 1876, when he spoke by phone to
his assistant in another room; that same year, at the centennial
exposition in Philadelphia, he presented his invention to the world

▲ A drawing of a human
embryo by Ernst Haeckel, a German
biologist, naturalist and artist, from his
Anthropogenie on the evolutionary
history of man, first published in 1876;
Haeckel's compatriot, the biologist
Oskar Hertwig, had shed new light on
reproduction in 1875, when he
established that embryos result from
a male sperm fertilising a female egg

a more general desire to spread far and wide the benefits of this
brave new world. As society embraced modernity, so it became
more democratic. Sport was opened up for mass participation
while the bicycle offered practically everyone an inexpensive way

► The American inventor Thomas Alva Edison – one of the most prolific innovators of any era – who once famously remarked that 'genius is one per cent inspiration and 99 per cent perspiration'

► In 1880 Edison patented the incandescent electric lamp, in which a carbon filament glowed white hot when the bulb was switched on; the bulb had a life of 40 hours

◄ In 1877 Edison and his collaborators devised the phonograph and the miracle of reproducing sound became a reality; flat shellac discs began to replace the original cylinders at the end of the 19th century

of getting about. Meanwhile, everyday items that would become icons of the next century – the vacuum cleaner, the fridge, Levi jeans – made their debuts towards the end of the 19th. Some key inventions of the period were to change people's lives forever.

▲ The French Michaux velocipede of 1861 was the first bicycle fitted with pedals and brakes, but the definitive step towards the modern bicycle was taken in 1879 by British engineer Henry Lawson when he introduced the 'safety' bicycle with a chain driving a sprocket on the rear wheel

▼ In 1879 American bar owner James Ritty took out a patent for the world's first cash register, which he christened the 'Incorruptible'

► Built upstream of London's main dockland area, Tower Bridge has a central span that opens to allow ocean-going ships into the Pool of London; when the bridge was first completed in 1894, London was a centre of industry as well as commerce, the biggest and busiest city in the world

The telephone meant that people no longer had to meet in person to converse. The phonograph would spread the sound of music, just as the printing press had spread the written word. And finally, the dynamo and the light bulb ushered in the age of electricity.

THE STORY OF INVENTIONS

The late 19th century seemed blessed with
an inexhaustible supply of raw materials.
Coal and iron – so vital to the early Industrial
Revolution – now combined to produce steel in
quantities that ensured the continued growth
of transport and industry. Slagheaps, pithead
winding gear and blast furnaces were now a
visible part of Europe's industrial landscape.
Meanwhile, oil derricks became a familiar sight
in many parts of the world as crude oil began
to flow from huge untapped reserves. Refined
into petroleum and other products, oil was
set to become the most important energy
resource of the next century.

THE BESSEMER PROCESS – 1856

Ushering in the age of steel

How to make steel had been known since ancient times, but it remained a small-scale industry until the British engineer Henry Bessemer came up with a process suited to industrial-scale manufacturing.

Foundry workers
These two illustrations (right) show steel-making around the turn of the 19th century. Molten metal is drawn off the blast furnace and poured into moulds (top). Later, this initial 'pig iron' is reheated in the forge then worked on an anvil (bottom).

Renaissance metal
Blast furnaces (below), as depicted in an engraving from De la Pirotechnica, *a treatise on metallurgy by Vannocio Biringuccio dating from 1558.*

At a meeting of the British Association for the Advancement of Science held in Cheltenham on 13 August, 1856, the inventor Henry Bessemer unveiled his revolutionary new process for manufacturing steel. There was nothing actually new about the material itself; people had known about it for at least two millennia. The ancient Greeks, for instance, hardened the blades of their iron swords by tempering them for hours in red-hot cinders; and they gave the resulting metal a completely new name. For centuries, metalworking was a home-grown operation, with steel being just one of the by-products, a kind of super-iron whose precise method of manufacture was far from clear. The significance of Bessemer's process was that it could produce steel in a predictable, controlled and reliable fashion, in large quantities and at a reasonable cost.

Fineries, puddling and crucible steel
In 1852 the American ironmaster William Kelly of Kentucky pioneered a new process for smelting steel that involved blowing air through molten iron to burn off the impurities

FROM FINERY FORGES TO BLAST FURNACES

Medieval blacksmiths produced limited quantities of steel by smelting iron ore and charcoal together in small furnaces. The initial product of smelting was called a 'bloom', a porous mass of iron and slag that was removed from the furnace and compacted by hammering it while still hot and malleable. By the 14th century this laborious task had been made easier by the use of bellows and trip hammers driven by waterwheels. As furnaces grew in size, the temperatures they could reach rose to 1200°C, hot enough to smelt alloys of iron and carbon. The resulting pig iron was worked into either wrought iron or steel. The first known blast furnace was built in Liège in Belgium in the late 1300s. The great advantage of this method was that smelting could carry on continuously. Fuel (charcoal) and iron ore were put in through the top of the furnace, and the molten iron or steel was collected at the base.

In 1709 Abraham Darby built the world's first coke-fired blast furnace at Coalbrookdale in Shropshire. By the 1780s, coke had supplanted charcoal as the most common fuel used in furnaces in Britain. The following century, blast furnaces reached some 30 metres in height. A modern blast furnace can produce 5,000–10,000 tonnes of iron or steel daily.

SMELTING IN INDIA AND CHINA

The Chinese used blast furnaces from as early as c1000 BC to fire and glaze pottery. During the Warring States period (476–221 BC), blast furnaces began to be used for making cast iron, which was then worked into wrought iron and steel. In southern India in around AD 300, blacksmiths started to produce a very hard form of steel, used primarily for making sabre blades. This 'Wootz steel' (a term coined by the British metallurgist Benjamin Heyne) involved two stages: first came the smelting of iron ore to produce cast iron; this was then reheated at high temperature in a fire-resistant crucible with wrought iron, charcoal and glass. The resulting 'buttons' of steel were separated from the slag and forged into ingots. The hardness of Wootz steel came from traces of vanadium present in the iron ore that was mined in southern India. The end product was highly sought after and sold as far afield as the Middle East. There it became known as Damascus steel and was much in demand for making sword blades that were renowned for their durability. Production of Wootz steel continued until the 18th century, when the seams of native iron ore became exhausted.

in it. His method anticipated Bessemer – indeed, the two men came at the problem from the same angle and there was little to choose between the techniques. The key advantage of the British inventor's method was that it enabled steel to be made on an industrial scale.

Before 1856 there were different ways of making steel. In Germany, northern France and Wallonia (the French-speaking region of Belgium) the traditional method was known as the finery forge. This entailed remelting pig iron tapped from a blast furnace so as to oxidise the carbon and produce bars of wrought iron. These bars were placed with charcoal in long stone pots and reheated in a furnace in order to convert them into steel. From 1783 onwards, the finery forge process was replaced by 'puddling', a technique

invented by English ironmaster Henry Cort which represented the first step towards the industrialisation of steelmaking. From around 1740, though, another method had taken root in certain British iron and steelmaking centres such as Sheffield and Newcastle. This involved slowly heating and cooling pure iron and carbon (in the form of charcoal) inside sealed pots or 'crucibles', which were left for several days in a coke-fired furnace.

A chance discovery

Henry Bessemer's starting point for his invention was an attempt to improve the reverberatory furnace in which puddling took place. In this type of furnace, the material being smelted is not allowed to come directly into contact with the fuel, but instead is exposed to hot gases reflecting back off the walls of an arched combustion chamber. One day, during a test firing, Bessemer noticed that some ingots of pig iron that had not been properly submerged in the smelting ladle had been converted into steel simply through contact with the hot air of the furnace. This chance discovery convinced him that he could 'carburise' pig iron – that is, remove impurities, especially carbon, from it – through oxidation, the action of air, without first having to smelt it into wrought iron. Another bonus was that no extra fuel would be required, since the reaction generated its own heat. And so he set about designing a converter in which molten pig iron could be transformed into steel by a current of high-pressure air.

Bessemer built a series of experimental smelting chambers incorporating multiple channels (known as 'tuyères') to force air into the vessel. First results were disappointing; even when the smelter managed to withstand the initial shock of the reaction, the problem was that the reaction died down too soon, leaving most of the pig iron inside still in its raw state. To stop the molten metal from shooting out and also, most importantly, to minimise heat loss, Bessemer realised that he needed to make a closed converter. But it had to be designed in such a way that the operators could still intervene if something went wrong. At this point, as Bessemer himself recalled in

Indian metal
An illustration from a 16th-century Portuguese manuscript shows Indian blacksmiths at work (below left).

Melting pot
A prototype Bessemer converter, made in 1855, already shows the characteristic retort shape. The first Bessemer converter to go into service was installed in the inventor's own steelworks in Sheffield in 1859.

Highly durable
This section of Bessemer steel (above) was cut from a cannon barrel then crushed with a steam hammer, with no signs of cracking.

Fiery hell
A painting of the 1880s shows a Bessemer retort in operation in a foundry in Pittsburgh in the USA. A 19th-century commentator called the steel city 'hell with the lid off'.

NEGLECTED BY HISTORY

The first person to think of injecting air into molten iron to increase the smelting temperature was not Henry Bessemer but an American named William Kelly. In doing so, Kelly – a salesman who became a forgemaster later in life – was not aiming to produce steel but rather to reduce charcoal usage. Blast furnaces were rapidly using up the virgin forests on the eastern seaboard of the USA and the spiralling cost of charcoal was fast making cast iron smelting unviable. So, between 1851–6, Kelly developed an 'air-boiling' process very similar to the process developed by Bessemer, but he kept his experiments secret. In 1856 he was shocked to learn that his British rival had already lodged a patent. Kelly protested, published his findings and was finally granted a patent in 1857, but he failed to have Bessemer's patent revoked. That same year, the two competing patents were jointly licensed for steelmaking at the Cambria Iron Works at Johnstown in Pennsylvania, the world's first giant steelworks, where Kelly was employed. Bessemer got the lion's share of royalties – perhaps because he was already well-known.

his autobiography, he hit on the brilliant idea of 'mounting the converter on trunnions' so that the entire vessel could be tipped to disgorge its contents at the end of the smelting process. The Bessemer converter (or Bessemer retort) was born – a huge ovoid metal container with a spout set obliquely at the top.

The steel age

It would take Bessemer a further two years to realise that his process did not effectively rid the pig iron of phosphorus, which made the resulting steel brittle. From 1858 onwards – the year in which he founded the Henry Bessemer and Co. Steelworks in Sheffield – he got round this problem by using only low-phosphorus pig iron sourced in England or Sweden. Meanwhile, British metallurgist Robert Mushet introduced some significant improvements, chief among which was the

MULTITUDE OF METALS

Iron, cast iron and steel all derive from the same basic oxides of iron contained in iron ore. They differ in the proportion of carbon and other elements added to them: a small amount of carbon produces a soft iron (malleable but not at all durable), whereas large amounts of carbon result in cast iron, which is hard but brittle. Middling amounts of carbon produce steel, which is highly durable. Nowadays, there are hundreds of different types of steel on the market, which differ in the amount of carbon they contain or through being alloyed with small quantities of metals like chrome or tungsten. These lend them new properties, such as extreme toughness or greater resistance to rusting.

Steel town
A lithograph of 1845 by John Rutherford shows the Cyclops Steel Works in Sheffield, founded in the 1840s. In the foreground run the tracks and trains of the busy Midland Railway. From the late 18th century onwards, Sheffield in South Yorkshire became famous the world over as a steelmaking town.

Engineering marvel
The Brooklyn Bridge, one of the first steel bridges, spans the East River in New York between Manhattan and Brooklyn. At 1,825m, it was the world's longest bridge when it opened in 1883; it is seen here in 1894.

addition of small amounts of manganese (in the form of the mineral alloy spiegeleisen) to make the finished steel easier to roll. The Swede G F Göransson discovered that low-pressure blasts of air produced a more complete and uniform smelting.

Demand for steel rocketed. Steel rails replaced less reliable cast iron on the railways. Shipbuilders now riveted together hulls from steel plates. Steel girders made it possible to construct huge new bridges like the Forth Railway Bridge, a cantilever structure spanning the Firth of Forth at a total length of 2,528m.

Soon, steel-framed skyscrapers were soaring above cities like New York and Chicago.

From the late 19th century onwards, steel also began to supply the raw material for weapons of war – cannons, howitzers, battleships and, in the First World War, tanks. The economic and military might of the major powers was gauged in terms of the quantities of steel they produced annually. In the 1890s Great Britain still led the world in steel production, but as the new century dawned it would be caught up and then outstripped by both Germany and the USA.

Open hearth *An 1898 painting by Marcello Nizzoli shows Siemens-Martin furnaces at the Italian Ansaldo steelworks.*

RIVAL STEELMAKING PROCESSES

The fact that the Bessemer converter could not rid steel of phosphorus hampered the spread of the process in countries where the iron ore was rich in this mineral, including Germany, France, Belgium, Luxembourg and Wales. In 1876 two cousins, Sidney Gilchrist Thomas and Percy Gilchrist, solved the problem by lining converters with dolomite, a sedimentary rock rich in alkaline lime, which effectively neutralised the acidic phosphorus oxides in the iron ores. For good measure, in the Thomas–Gilchrist process lime was also added to the mixture of ores, coke and pig iron in the converter.

Cast iron becomes liquid at around 1200°C, whereas the melting point of iron is much higher, at 1535°C. Traditional reverberatory furnaces could not produce such high temperatures, but in 1864 the French inventor Pierre-Emile Martin devised a gas-fired furnace capable of melting iron ore and steel and iron scrap. His design was based on the regenerative furnace invented by the German Wilhelm Siemens in 1856, which achieved a higher temperature by burning previously unburnt gases. The resulting Siemens–Martin or 'open-hearth' process yielded a high-quality steel that was ideal for making armaments or wheels for railway rolling stock. It also enabled all kinds of scrap metal to be reused, while the length of the process allowed for better quality control.

THE REMARKABLE RÉAUMUR

An early contributor to the understanding of iron and steel was the French scholar René Antoine de Réaumur (1683–1757), a true son of the Enlightenment whose wide-ranging interests included metallurgy. In 1722 he set out the results of his experiments with ferrous metals in a work that was translated into English as *The art of converting cast iron into steel and of rendering cast iron ductile*. One important conclusion he came to was that steel contained traces of other minerals, especially carbon, that gave the metal its durability. Réaumur had a special furnace built lined with heat-resistant bricks to produce steel by the cementation or tempering process, involving heating wrought iron and charcoal together in an airtight container. The technique remained popular for a long time among British steelmakers. Not only did Réaumur demonstrate the key role played by carbon in the hardness of steel, but he was also the first to study the structure of metals produced by cementation; his work in this area laid the foundations of the science of metallography.

German arms giant
Workers at the Krupp steelworks in Essen (right) forging the barrel for a cannon in 1900. This massive steelworks was in operation until the 1960s.

Malleable metal
Red-hot sheet steel on a rolling mill in a modern foundry (below). Once it has hardened, steel can be made malleable again by reheating it and passing it through a rolling mill. This manufacturing technique is used to produce steel plate or tubing.

NEANDERTHAL MAN
Unearthing human ancestry

Where exactly Neanderthal Man fits on the human genealogical tree still remains a mystery today, more than 150 years after remains of this early hominid were first found. One thing is certain: in contrast to the clichéd view of Neanderthals as primitive, brutal creatures, they had highly developed cognitive and technical skills.

Prehistoric burial
The Neanderthal skeleton uncovered in a cave at La Chapelle-aux-Saints in 1908 (top right). Palaeontologists have dated the remains to between 43,000 and 35,000 BC, making it one of the earliest human burial sites ever discovered.

In August 1856, workers digging in a lime quarry in the Neander Valley near the German city of Düsseldorf came across a perfectly preserved skull cap. They showed it to a local maths teacher and keen amateur naturalist, Johann Fuhlrott, who immediately realised how extraordinary the find was. The skull clearly was not that of a bear as the workers had first thought, but with a low forehead and prominent suborbital brow ridge it resembled no creature then known. The saga of Neanderthal Man had begun.

The skull caused a furore among the scientific community. These were the first known fossilised remains of an extinct species of human to come to light. In the absence of reliable dating methods (which were only developed from the 1930s onwards), people talked in vague terms about an 'antediluvian man'. The species was given its scientific name (*Homo neanderthalensis*) in 1864. Influenced by the racial and political prejudices of the time, scientists came up with some outlandish theories on the origins of the Neanderthal remains, variously claiming them to be those of a Cossack deserter from the Russian army, a degenerate idiot, or – according to the eminent British biologist Thomas Huxley in 1863 – a primitive hominid of an inferior racial type represented among living humans by Australian Aborigines. This image of an inferior being was to prove extremely tenacious.

Skull cap
The cranium found in the Neander Valley in 1856. A Neanderthal skull differs from that of a modern human in having an elongated and voluminous brain case, a sharply receding forehead and extremely large, deep eye sockets.

Rehabilitating Neanderthal Man

Subsequent finds of fossilised remains of early forms of *Homo sapiens* – notably the discovery of Cro-Magnon man in the Dordogne region of France in 1868 – cast new light on the Neanderthals. It became clear that the two species had probably coexisted in distant prehistory. Then, in 1908, a complete Neanderthal skeleton was unearthed at La Chapelle-aux-Saints in central France. The position and posture of the skeleton indicated that it had been intentionally buried.

In the 20th century and into the 21st, palaeontology – the study of ancient organisms through their fossilised remains – has revealed much more about Neanderthals. They were a

---

FAR AND WIDE

Some 300 finds of Neanderthal fossil remains from more than a hundred separate sites show that this human species colonised a huge area, stretching from the Atlantic coast of Europe to Siberia, taking in the Middle East. In 2008 palaeontologists compared traces of strontium (a radioactive element) from the tooth enamel of Neanderthal fossils found at the Lakonis site in southern Greece with isotopes of the same element from various water sources in the surrounding area. These showed that the Neanderthals who lived there some 40,000 years ago must have regularly drunk water from a source more than 20km from their camp.

In the flesh
From the 1990s onwards advances in medical and forensic facial reconstruction, combined with 3D computer imaging, have enabled scientists to re-create the features of prehistoric species from their bone structure, including the face of Neanderthal Man (left).

WHY DID THE NEANDERTHALS DISAPPEAR?

One theory as to why the Neanderthals, who had thrived for some 300 millennia, were supplanted by our own species around 30,000 years ago is that they were struck down by an unknown epidemic. Possible evidence for this comes from severe deformations in the cranial bones of some skeletons. Another hypothesis blames their extinction on violent territorial conflict with *Homo sapiens*, but as yet no archaeological evidence has been found to support this claim. A third theory currently gaining ground among researchers is that Neanderthal Man was less versatile than *Homo sapiens* and so was unable to adapt to the major and increasingly frequent climatic changes that were affecting the Earth around the time the species became extinct.

sturdy, thick-set human species with a cranial capacity equal to or even larger than our own. They had mastered highly advanced cognitive and technical skills, as demonstrated, for example, by finds of bifacial cutting tools and scrapers at Lehrlingen in Lower Saxony and of finely tapered spears, over 2 metres long, at the nearby site of Schöningen. Other finds revealed that they had developed sophisticated religious rites. In a grave at Shanidar in Iraqi Kurdistan, which was excavated in 1960, the body of a Neanderthal adult male had been interred beneath a carpet of flowers, evidently as part of an elaborate burial ritual.

Now that Neanderthal Man has been accorded the status of ancestral hominid, with technical and social skills pointing to language use, scientists are struggling to place the species on the human genealogical tree. Did Neanderthals interbreed with *Homo sapiens*,

making it a human subspecies, or were they a distinct species? To answer this question researchers at the Max Planck Institute in Leipzig have been comparing DNA sequences from Neanderthal fossils with those of modern humans. Preliminary findings suggest two distinct species, though not all scientists agree with this interpretation of the data.

Human neighbours
Neanderthal Man (above, left) and Cro-Magnon Man (right) coexisted for more than 12,000 years.

ARTIFICIAL DYES – 1856
Marvellous mauve

It was purely by chance that a young British chemistry student discovered how to synthesise mauveine, the world's first artificial dye. The lucky discovery made its inventor a fortune.

Precious purple
Three vials of the original mauveine dye produced by William Perkin (right).

In March 1856 William Henry Perkin, an 18-year-old chemistry student, was spending his Easter break in a makeshift laboratory in his London flat. Responding to a challenge set by his professor at the Royal College of Chemistry, the German chemist August Wilhelm von Hofmann, he was trying to synthesise quinine, the only known remedy against the malaria that was then rife in parts of the British Empire.

Like most chemists of the time, Perkin began by using coal tar – a by-product either of the carbonisation of coal in making coke or its gasification into coal gas. From this raw material he produced an organic compound known as aniline. Perkin chose this substance as the starting point for his research because its overall chemical composition was very similar to that of quinine. Oxidising the aniline with potassium dichromate, he obtained a reddish-black precipitation. When he poured ethanol into the flask to clean it, it was transformed into an intense purple-coloured solution.

The end product of Perkin's experiment was no good for treating malaria, but he noticed that it left an indelible stain when it came into contact with fabrics. This gave him the idea of using it to make an artificial dye. He recruited his brother Thomas and a friend, Arthur Church, and they set about improving

his 'aniline purple'. When they were finally satisfied with the formula, they sent a sample to a silk dyeworks in Perth, Scotland. Almost by return of post they received an urgent request for more. Perkin duly filed for a patent for his invention on 26 August, 1856.

A long history

Perkin was by no means the first to realise the potential of synthetic products as dyestuffs. In 1771 the Irish chemist Peter Woulfe produced picric acid, a bright yellow dye that was used for colouring silks, by adding nitric acid to indigo. Although it was based on a natural vegetable dye, many people consider this to be the world's first artificial dye.

In 1826 the German chemist and merchant Otto Unverdorben became the first person to isolate aniline, which he obtained through distilling indigo. He named his discovery 'crystalline'. Eight years later, his compatriot Friedrich Ferdinand Runge extracted a substance from coal tar that turned a beautiful blue colour when it was treated with chloride

---

A PRECOCIOUS CHILD

As the son of an East End boat-builder, there was nothing in William Perkin's background to suggest that he might one day make his fortune in synthetic dyes. He was, however, an extremely precocious child. At the City of London school, he became keen on chemistry through the work of Michael Faraday. Aged 15, Perkin won a place at the Royal College of Chemistry, where he was appointed as an assistant to the director August Wilhelm von Hofmann. By the time he sold his dye business – after making millions of pounds – he was still only 36 years old. He devoted the rest of his life to research, particularly into perfumes. He synthesised coumarin, an artificial aroma very similar to vanilla, and made many important new discoveries regarding the modification of organic molecules. He died in 1907, having received a knighthood and numerous academic honours.

of lime – this aniline dye was called 'cyanol'. In 1841, also in Germany, C J Fritzsche showed that if indigo was treated with caustic potash (potassium carbonate) it yielded an oily substance that he called 'aniline' (the specific name for one indigo-producing plant is *Indigofera anil*). Around the same time a Russian chemist, N N Zinin, found that if nitrobenzene was reduced it formed a base that he named 'benzidam'. In 1855 August Wilhelm von Hofmann demonstrated that all four of these differently prepared substances had an identical molecular structure.

Birth of an industry

Perkin's great achievement was becoming the first person to manufacture artificial dyes on an industrial scale. He first devised a way to make the dye colour-fast on cotton fabrics, then created a whole series of dyes based on aniline, such as Britannia Violet and Perkin Green. In 1857 he gave up his chemistry studies and established a family firm on the banks of the Grand Junction Canal in Greenford, west London. People living nearby reported that the water changed colour every week according to which

NATURAL DYES

Before William Perkin came on the scene, textiles were coloured with natural dyes made from plants, minerals or animals. Many had been used since the earliest times, including indigo (extracted from plants of the *Indigofera* genus), dyer's madder and henna (both from plants of the same name), and carmine (from cochineal bugs). Tyrian purple, the most expensive dye, came from the sea snail *Murex brandaris*. The drawback was that many natural dyes were unstable.

Pl. 153.
Garance des teinturiers. Rubia tinctorum L.

Natural bounty
Since ancient times, various plants, minerals and animals have been the source of dyes, including the Murex *sea snail (far left) which coloured the purple robes of Roman emperors; roots of the madder plant (left), which produced a bright red colour; and the leaves of* Indigofera *plants, native to India (above).*

29

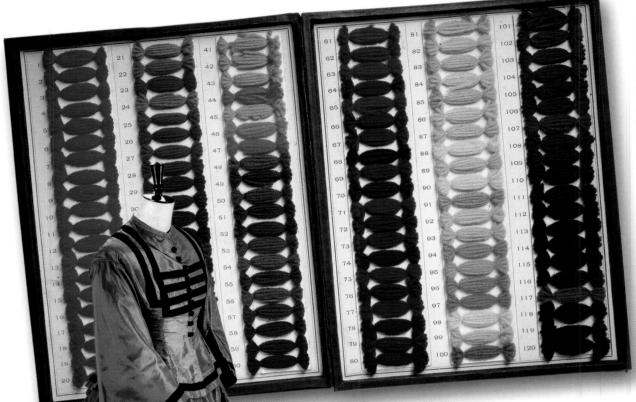

Box of colours
A range of dyed wool samples from 1910 (left). The production of artifical dyes shot up from nothing before 1856 to 15,000 tons a year by 1873.

Victorian elegance
This dress once worn by Queen Victoria was dyed with Perkin's fashionable mauveine.

dye was being produced. Perkin's venture was perfectly timed. Purple was all the rage, thanks to fashionable royal courts like that of Napoleon III of France and his consort, the Empress Eugénie, who favoured fabrics dyed with mauveine (the English word 'mauve' was coined in 1859, from the French term for the mallow flower). Demand was also boosted because the full-length dresses and crinolines then in fashion used huge amounts of cloth. On the supply side, Britain was rich in coal and turning out vast quantities of Perkin's raw material: coal tar. He was soon a millionaire. The crowning moment for his enterprise came in 1862, when Queen Victoria attended the Royal Exhibition in a silk gown dyed with mauveine. Even when mauve went out of fashion at the end of the decade, Perkin kept ahead of the market by offering all the colours of the rainbow in synthetic dyes.

Within a short time, chemists throughout Europe discovered dozens of other artificial dyes deriving from aniline. These included magenta, which was invented by the French chemist François Verguin and rivalled mauve in its popularity. Others included Bismarck brown – from Germany, naturally – aniline yellow and Hofmann violet.

Perkin sold his business in 1874. The company is now a major pharmaceutical concern, trading under the name of Zeneca. As for quinine, where the story began, it was eventually synthesised in 1944 by the American chemists Robert Burns Woodward and William von Eggers Doering. It would be 1994 before the molecular structure of mauveine was correctly established as four related aromatic compounds.

FATHER OF ORGANIC CHEMISTRY

In 1828 the German chemist Friedrich Wöhler (1800–82) took a groundbreaking step by proving that organic and inorganic compounds may contain the same elements. By heating ammonium cyanate (a mineral), he obtained urea, an organic compound that is found in the urine of mammals and amphibians. His discovery not only paved the way for the development of synthetic dyestuffs (many derived from thiourea), artificial fertilisers and food supplements for livestock, but also laid the foundations of organic chemistry.

Condensed milk 1857

In its natural state, milk only keeps for a short time and does not travel well. Over the course of the 19th century, with the growing exodus from the country to the city, the consumption of milk fell drastically. The first successful attempt to create a more longlife form of milk came in 1857, a full decade before the advent of pasteurisation. It was the invention of a Texas farmer named Gail Borden (1801–74), who was concerned to prevent malnutrition among children. Natural milk contains 87 per cent water; by heating

THE MILK RUSH

Gail Borden's sweetened condensed milk was an instant hit, thanks in part to the American Civil War. Vast quantities were orded by the Union as part of the rations provided for Union soldiers. The milk's long life also made it popular with homesteaders and prospectors who began to settle the American West from the 1850s onwards.

milk in a vacuum pan, Borden found a way to reduce the water content, producing a condensed (or concentrated) milk which, after sugar had been added, kept for much longer. Unsweetened concentrated milk was introduced in 1881. In 1998, the merger of Borden's company with the firm founded by the Swiss industrialist Henri Nestlé created a multinational giant.

Hungry mouths
An advertisement of c1887 for Gail Borden's 'Eagle Brand' condensed milk. When he created the product he had children like these in mind, especially those living in cities and towns.

Toilet paper 1857

Since time immemorial, people have devised various means of cleansing themselves after answering the call of nature. In ancient Rome, for example, they used a wet sponge on a stick, while in India and Arabia water applied by hand was the preferred method. Other peoples have used leaves or clumps of moss. The earliest historically attested use of toilet paper was at the imperial court in 14th-century China. The mass production of toilet paper began in 1857 in America, the brainchild of inventor Joseph Cayetty. At 50 cents for 500 sheets, it was an expensive luxury. Cayetty's product, which was impregnated with aloe as a lubricant, was originally marketed as a medical aid against haemorroids. The Scott Paper Company of America began producing rolls of toilet paper from 1879 onwards. The term 'toilet paper' was coined by the *New York Times* in 1888. Gradually, as the price of toilet tissue fell, it replaced the improvised solution of torn-up newspaper.

ENVIRONMENTALLY UNFRIENDLY

Europeans use an average of 13kg of toilet paper per person each year. According to ecological campaign groups, worldwide demand for toilet paper accounts for the felling of around 270,000 trees a day. To try to limit this impact, consumers are being encouraged to switch to recycled paper, while some manufacturers plant a new tree for each one felled.

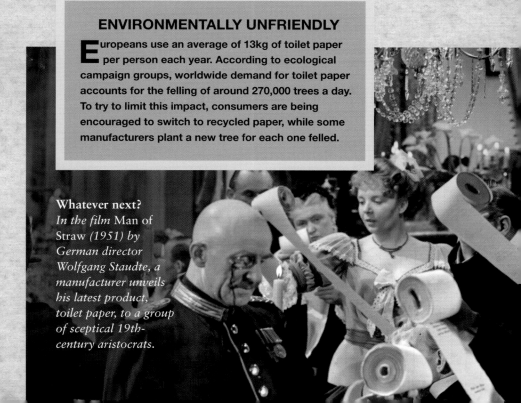

Whatever next?
In the film Man of Straw *(1951) by German director Wolfgang Staudte, a manufacturer unveils his latest product, toilet paper, to a group of sceptical 19th-century aristocrats.*

OIL EXTRACTION – 1859
Black gold starts to flow

Oil is the most widely exploited energy source in the world today, but back in the 1850s it was only being extracted piecemeal for use as fuel in lamps. Then Edwin Drake began drilling in Pennsylvania.

Let there be light
An Egyptian lamp from the 1st century AD (above right), one of the oldest lamps ever found. Originally, it would have been filled with mineral oil.

By the end of August 1859, Edwin Drake was teetering on the edge of a financial abyss. For a month, he had not received a single cent from his backers at the Seneca Oil Company and the shopkeepers in Titusville, Pennsylvania, were now refusing him credit. If he did not strike oil soon, he would be ruined.

'A very valuable product'

Drake's adventure with oil had begun two years earlier when he was working as a conductor on the trains between New York and New Haven, Connecticut. One day, at a New Haven hotel, he made the acquaintance of businessman James M Townsend, who was

Shared venture
A share certificate for the Seneca Oil Company, as the Pennsylvania Rock Oil Company was known from 1858.

impressed by Drake's entrepreneurial spirit and diverse experience. He offered Drake a stake in a new oil venture. In 1854, Townsend had founded the Pennsylvania Rock Oil Company (PROC) with a group of business associates. They had an eye to exploiting the commercial potential of 'rock oil', a natural resource that occurred in the west of the state. As yet no-one had identified a market for the product, also known as 'petroleum oil', although it was

---

CAULKING AND GREEK FIRE

Because bitumen naturally bubbles up through oil-shale rocks at various places on the Earth's surface, oil has been known and used since ancient times. The peoples of Mesopotamia caulked the hulls of their boats with thick, tarry bitumen to make them watertight. The substance was also employed as mortar in ramparts built with fired mud bricks. And despite the acrid smell that it gave off when burned, unrefined mineral oil was used from earliest times as a source of light. The ancient Egyptians also used pitch, primarily as a preserving agent when mummifying bodies. The Middle Ages witnessed the invention of a terrifying weapon based on pitch – an early form of napalm known as 'Greek fire'. The Byzantine Empire deployed it to devastating effect in its frequent wars against the Seljuk Turks. Terracotta grenades were filled with a mixture of pitch and saltpetre; when launched from a ship, they exploded in mid-air, spreading a sheet of flame on the water and incinerating any enemy vessels that were engulfed by it. In 15th-century Europe and North America, oil was thought to have curative properties and was used as a remedy for many aches and pains.

used by the local Seneca Indians as a salve for rheumatic pains and as a mosquito repellent.

At that time, the main fuel used in domestic and miners' lamps was still whale oil, which was also widely used as an industrial lubricant. But the slaughter required to fulfil the demand for oil meant that the number of whales in the seas was rapidly dwindling – and the price of oil was rocketing. In 1854, a Canadian chemist named Abraham Gesner filed a patent for the industrial manufacture of kerosene. Created by distilling solid hydrocarbons such as bitumen (or coal – another name for it was 'coal oil'), kerosene burned with a bright flame and little

Handful of wealth

Oil is one of the principal pillars of the global economic system.
The world's major producer is Saudi Arabia, followed closely by
Russia and the USA.

FINITE RESOURCE

Oil is created by the decomposition of organic matter – primarily vegetation – through the action of bacteria. Over many millennia, masses of plant debris accumulated and rotted down in damp, confined locations such as lakes, lagoons and deltas, then this organic matter was gradually covered up by sediment. As the layers of soil built up, exerting pressure on layers beneath, so the plant matter began to ferment. It took several millions of years at temperatures of 60–120°C and depths of between 1,500 to 4,000 metres to transform the plant matter into oil. This process of transformation still goes on today, but the timescales involved are such that only existing oil deposits will be of any use to humanity. Some 110 billion tonnes of oil are thought to have already been extracted. It is hard to estimate what reserves are left, since this depends to a large extent on how exploration and drilling techniques develop, but most experts agree that some 140 to 160 billion tonnes remain to be exploited. At current rates of consumption, these deposits will last for only another 60 years.

smoke. Gesner's development galvanised prospective oilmen into action and a Yale chemistry professor, one Benjamin Silliman Jr, was hired to distil rock oil to see whether it could also yield lamp oil. By breaking the crude oil down into several fractions, he obtained a substance that gave off a strong light when burned in a lamp. Silliman concluded that his 'petroleum' – in actual fact it was a lighter distillation product called naphtha – was a 'raw material from which ... they may manufacture a very valuable product'.

Townsend and his associates needed no further prompting. Naphtha clearly had a future as a lamp fuel and their enterprise appeared potentially to be a very profitable venture. The only problem was that crude oil was difficult to extract. The deposits owned by the PROC were at the small settlement of Titusville, where a mixture of water and oil

Oil strike

Edwin Drake's efforts were finally rewarded on 29 August, 1859, when oil began to flow from his drillings at the Titusville field (above left).

Wooden rig
Edwin Drake (on the right) and his associate Peter Wilson (left) in front of the derrick at 'Oil Creek' in the Titusville field in Pennsylvania. It was the first oil well in the USA.

UNJUST DESERTS

Although the oil drilling technique pioneered by Edwin Drake is still widely used today, it did not earn him a single cent during his lifetime. His cardinal error was to fail to submit a patent, which would undoubtedly have made him a multi-millionaire. In 1860, after the Seneca Oil Company had repaid his hard work, loyalty and expertise by sacking him, Drake set up a rival company to exploit and sell mineral oil reserves. But a sudden price slump wiped out his savings and he found himself facing financial ruin. In 1873 he was saved from complete destitution by the State of Pennsylvania, which granted him a pension in recognition of his 'major contribution to the growth of the oil industry'. Edwin Drake died in 1880 at the age of 61.

seeped up to the surface from the subsoil, forming viscous ponds. The traditional method of collection had simply been to skim the ponds by dipping rags into them to soak up the oil and then wringing them out. The PROC had improved on this somewhat by installing a pipe that pumped the oil off as it rose to the surface. Yet this still only succeeded in producing a handful of barrels every few months. This was where Drake came in; the company dispatched him to increase the yield.

Striking lucky

Drake arrived at Titusville in December 1857. In May of the following year, after a period spent scouting out the region, he quit his job on the railroad and moved into the village. To try to extract the oil, he began by digging shallow trenches, but to no avail. It was at this juncture that one of Townsend's partners, the lawyer George Bissell, suggested to Drake that he drill the kind of well that had traditionally been sunk to obtain brine (salt water). In Kentucky in 1829, for instance, an oil gusher had occurred accidentally while workmen were digging just such a well.

Accordingly, Drake visited a blacksmith named William Smith in Tarentum, northwest Pennsylvania, who was an expert in drilling brine wells. He persuaded Smith and his sons to move to Titusville and they commenced operations in the summer of 1859, constructing a wooden tower (a derrick) to support their drilling tool, a rock-cutting drill bit suspended from a cable. An old steam engine powered a rocker mechanism fitted with metal weights that drove the bit down into the bedrock.

Drake was impressed by Smith's know-how, but the Titusville operation was beset by problems. No sooner had drilling begun than the well filled up with water; the ground at the site, barely 50 metres from the creek, was just too waterlogged. Progress was painfully slow, and as the work dragged on for weeks without success, locals began to call the derrick 'Drake's Folly'. Then Drake had the brilliant idea of enclosing the drill bit in a metal pipe. Protected from the surrounding water, the drill cut through the soft ground far faster and soon reached the bedrock.

Even so, the investors of the Seneca Oil Company (as the PROC had become by that stage) were growing impatient. Finally, on 27 August, when the drill had reached a depth of 23 metres, it emerged covered in oil. It was not a spectacular gusher, but the news spread like wildfire. By the end of the year, the company was extracting 20 barrels a day, selling at 20 dollars apiece. Oil was clearly a

Playing with fire
One of the techniques used to get the oil flowing in the Pennsylvania fields in c1900 was to pour the explosive nitroglycerine into the head of a pile driver, which was then dropped down the well to blast away the rock cap above the deposit.

Horseless carriage
The internal combustion engine and the automobile opened up a new market for oil from the late 1880s onwards. This car was produced in 1902 by the Belgian small-arms firm Herstal, which diversified into manufacturing automobiles and motorbikes.

profitable business. Investors and prospectors alike prospered. One year later, 74 wells had been sunk, 35 of them in the valley where Drake began his operations. Titusville mushroomed from 125 inhabitants in 1859 to a population of 10,000 just five years later.

Growth of a major industry

By 1864, oil production in the United States had reached more than 6,000 barrels a day (the measurement of a barrel was standardised in the early Pennsylvania fields at 42 US gallons). In 1870, John D Rockefeller founded an oil refining concern in Cleveland, Ohio – the Standard Oil Company. With this development, the oil industry now truly began in earnest.

In 1879 the invention of the incandescent electric light bulb by Thomas Edison and Joseph Swan momentarily threatened this embryonic industry. But in 1885 Silliman devised a new method of fractional distillation, so creating a range of new products from oil: tars, lubricants, solvents for oil paints and, most importantly, petroleum, which at first was only used as a stain remover.

Before long, the invention of the internal combustion engine and the advent of the motor car gave oil a major role both industrially and in the transport sector. The new automobiles

DRILLING TECHNIQUES

The method that Edwin Drake used to drill his wells is known as 'cable-tool' or 'percussion' drilling. A drill bit was repeatedly dropped using a cable and pulley system, breaking the ground as it went. Rotary drilling, introduced in the 1920s, made for faster, deeper drilling: a heavy drill bit is attached to lengths of hollow drill pipe and as the well deepens additional pipes are attached at the top to make a 'drillstring'. Drillers have an array of tools to deal with different types of ground, from rock-hammers to three-wing 'drag bits' for clay soils. Offshore drilling began in the 1970s. So-called 'jack-up' rigs, with legs that rest on the seabed, are used in shallow waters (down to 120m);

semi-submersible floating rigs, held in place by seabed anchors, are used in deeper water (to 2,500m). Many formerly inaccessible parts of the world have now been opened up for oil exploration, although with disastrous results in 2010 when the Deepwater Horizon exploratory rig exploded then sank in the Gulf of Mexico, leaving crude oil and gas pouring into the sea. The future may lie in fields once thought to be exhausted; in some cases existing drilling techniques only managed to extract around 30 per cent of the reserves. New methods such as horizontal drilling or injecting carbon dioxide, steam or polymers into the oil-bearing strata can make it easier to pump the oil up to the wellhead.

Offshore rig
A drilling platform north of the Dutch island of Ameland in the North Sea (top right). Experts believe that undersea reserves represent half of all remaining oil reserves.

Fields of derricks
In the 1860s, the American oil industry comprised just 15 fields in Pennsylvania (left). Then oil was found in Virginia, Ohio and California. Today, US oil reserves are estimated at some 22.5 billion barrels. Estimates put total reserves worldwide at around 1,300 billion barrels, some 700 billion barrels of which are in the Middle East.

that appeared around the turn of the century ran on oil in the form of petrol or diesel, while aeroplanes used kerosene. Heavy fuel oil began to rival coal as a power source for ships, while paraffin was used to heat homes. From the 1940s onwards, oil also became the principal source of organic raw materials, giving rise to the petrochemical industry. Plastics, pharmaceuticals, detergents, paints, cosmetics, fertilisers, defoliants and insecticides are all derived wholly or in part from oil.

Oil production worldwide continued to increase, reaching more than 700 million barrels a year in 1920 and 3.2 billion barrels in 1945; today's figure is around 30 billion barrels a year. The influence of oil pervades almost every industrial sector and oil wealth can ensure a nation's prosperity. Economic growth is assured when oil is plentiful, whereas disruptions in supply and massive price increases destabilise the world's economy, as seen in the global oil crises of 1973 and 1979. In the 20th century, the human race hitched its fate to that of oil to such a degree that the prospect of oil reserves running out during the 21st century augurs profound and alarming changes in every sector of society.

THE SCRAMBLE FOR OIL

Before Edwin Drake's discovery of oil in Pennsylvania, the world's leading oil producer was Romania, with an output in 1857 of 275 tons, equivalent to 2,000 barrels. That same year, the Romanian capital Bucharest became the first city in the world to be lit by oil-fuelled street lamps. Oil drilling spread to Transylvania, Poland and Azerbaijan in the late 19th century. In 1885 the Rothschild banking dynasty began prospecting in Russia. Between 1901 and 1905, production mushroomed in the USA, as deposits were found in Texas, California and Oklahoma. Oil booms hit Mexico in 1910 and Venezuela in 1922. The Middle East, which is now thought to have more than half of remaining oil reserves, began production in 1901, when the British started prospecting in the Iranian desert. In neighbouring British-run Iraq, large-scale production began in 1927 after oil was found near Kirkuk. Kuwait and Saudi Arabia followed in 1938. In 1960, Saudi Arabia, Iraq, Iran, Kuwait and Venezuela formed the Organisation of the Petroleum Exporting Countries (OPEC), a cartel aimed at controlling worldwide oil prices.

Power house
Crude oil cannot be used in its raw state – it has to be processed, or refined, into fuels and lubricants. The largest oil refinery in the world is the Reliance Petroleum Company's plant at Jamnagar (above) in northwest India.

37

Darwin and 'The Origin of Species'

In the mid 19th century, a key tenet guiding all Judeo-Christian societies was that humankind – indeed, the Earth and all life on it – was created by God in accordance with the account given in the Book of Genesis. Then, in 1859, an English naturalist published the theory that evolution, rather than a single act of creation, lay behind the great diversity of species on the planet.

Seminal work
A first edition of Darwin's The Origin of Species, *published by John Murray (above right). Other authors whose works first appeared under this famous London imprint include Jane Austen, Lord Byron and Sir Walter Scott.*

On Thursday, 24 November, 1859, one of the most important books of all time, *On the Origin of Species by Means of Natural Selection*, was published in England. Its author, Charles Darwin (1809–82), was a 50-year-old natural historian well known in British scientific circles. He had been working on this, his magnum opus, for over 20 years. It was an instant sensation; within days, the entire first printing of 1,170 copies had been sold, creating uproar in the Church, the press and Victorian society.

Overturning orthodoxy

The ideas put forward in Darwin's work meant nothing less than a complete overthrow of the prevailing view of the world. In the mid-19th century, the traditional Biblical account of the origins of life still held sway in European societies. This taught that God had created the Earth and all that was in it – plants, animals and human beings – in six days. An attempt to work out the date when this had actually occurred reached a figure of around 6,000 years ago. To explain the existence of the fossils found in rock formations, some scientists embraced the 'catastrophist' theory of French palaeontologist Georges Cuvier (1769–1832). Cuvier maintained that there had been many phases of creation throughout geological time, but that each had been destroyed by a catastrophic event, the last being the Great Flood recounted in the Book of Genesis.

The doctrine of evolution

From the late 1830s onwards, Darwin had begun to question these orthodox views. On 11 January, 1844, he confided to his close friend, the botanist Joseph Hooker: 'I am almost convinced … that species are not immutable', adding '(it is almost like confessing

WALLACE AND DARWIN

Like Darwin, the British naturalist Alfred Russel Wallace (1823–1913; left) believed in evolutionary change. In a paper of 1855, Wallace first broached the idea of natural selection, proposing that 'every species has come into existence coincident both in space and time with a pre-existing closely allied species'. In June 1858 Darwin received a letter from Wallace, then in Indonesia, which revealed that he was pursuing the same ideas that Darwin had been working on secretly for 20 years.

Darwin's shock at the letter was compounded a few days later when his youngest son, Charles Waring Darwin, aged 18 months, was struck down by scarlet fever. On 1 July, two of Darwin's friends, Charles Lyell and Joseph Hooker, gave a joint reading of papers by Darwin and Wallace at the Linnean Society of London; the proceedings were published on 25 August. Spurred into action, Darwin released a one-volume summary of the essay he had been writing since 1842. This work became *The Origin of Species*. Wallace never held it against Darwin that he preempted him. He became an eminent scholar in his own right and a staunch advocate of Darwin's theories.

Famous vessel
A drawing of HMS Beagle *anchored off the coast of South America (left). The ship on which Darwin made his famous voyage to the Pacific, was a small vessel of 240 tons. Sailors nicknamed such ships 'coffin brigs' because they were prone to heeling over and sinking in rough seas.*

Natural selection
Giraffes with the longest necks can best survive spells of drought, since this allows them to reach the leaves on the highest, ungrazed branches of the acacia trees on which they feed.

a murder)'. He delayed publishing *The Origin of Species* for fear it might shock his friends and family, above all his wife Emma, who was a devout Christian. Even so, he believed he had found 'the simple way by which species become exquisitely adapted to various ends', as he explained to Hooker. This insight would eventually force him to overcome his reticence.

The Origin of Species outlined Darwin's ideas on the development of species, which he called a 'theory of descent with modifications' (he did not use the term 'evolution' until 1872). On the one hand, far from being immutable, species were constantly subject to incremental changes in their physiology and anatomy. On the other, the individuals that survived and reproduced were those that adapted to their environment through modifications that gave them an advantage, while others failed in the struggle for survival. This, in a nutshell, was the theory of natural selection, which lay at the root of the emergence of all new species.

In the footsteps of others

Like all scientific developments, Darwin's theory did not emerge from a vacuum. He was following in the footsteps of scholars who had already espoused the theory of 'transformism',

the notion that species could change over time. They included his own grandfather Erasmus Darwin (1731–1802) in his work *Zoonomia, or the Laws of Organic Life* (1794) and the French naturalists Jean-Baptiste de Monet Lamarck (1744–1829) in *Zoological Philosophy* (1809) and Étienne Geoffroy Saint-Hilaire (1772–1844) with his two-volume treatise *Anatomical Philosophy* (1818, 1822). Yet Darwin went much further in describing for the first time a mechanism that gave rise to the huge diversity of species, basing his theory on direct observations from nature.

Darwin had made these observations during his time as a naturalist on board the Royal Navy survey ship HMS *Beagle*, which set sail under Captain Robert FitzRoy in December 1831. On a round-the-world expedition, they visited the Canary Islands, South America, the Galápagos and Australia, returning home via the Cape of Good Hope to reach England in October 1836. Darwin, who was just 22 when the *Beagle* left Plymouth, became fascinated with the amazing diversity of life on Earth. In 1876 he wrote in

World of wonder
The Galápagos Islands, where Charles Darwin was inspired to some of his most momentous discoveries, became part of Ecuador in 1832. The islands were designated as a national park in 1959 and became a World Heritage Site in 1978.

his autobiography that 'the voyage of the *Beagle* was by far the most important event in my life and has determined my whole career'.

During the voyage, he read the first two volumes of the recently published *Principles of Geology* by Charles Lyell (1797–1875). In this work, Lyell argued against Cuvier's theory of catastrophism, subscribing instead to uniformitarianism, which proposed that the geological relics of past ages were formed by the same slow and gradual processes that were currently shaping the Earth. On reading Lyell's book, Darwin began to suspect that the Earth was far older than the 6,000 years cited from

Biblical sources and that small causes could, over the course of centuries and millennia, have very major effects.

Insight on the Galápagos

It would be another three years before Darwin formulated the idea of diversification of species, one of the main planks of his theory of evolution. In September and October of 1855, the *Beagle* visited four islands in the Galápagos Archipelago, which lie some 600 miles west of Ecuador in the Pacific Ocean. Darwin studied three different species of mocking bird, preserving several specimens. In *The Voyage of*

Important evidence
One of Darwin's specimens of Galápagos finch (Certhidea olivacea), *collected during his voyage on board the* Beagle.

1. Geospiza magnirostris
3. Geospiza parvula.

2. Geospiza fortis.
4. Certhidea olivacea.

the Beagle, his account of the expedition published in 1840, he recounted his findings: 'To my astonishment, I discovered that all those from Charles Island belonged to one species (*Mimus trifasciatus*); all from Albemarle Island to *M. parvulus*; and all from James and Chatham Islands belonged to *M. melanotis*.'

The species were quite distinct and yet also extremely similar to one another. This led Darwin to speculate that they were variants descended from a common ancestor native to the Americas, which diversified according to the demands of their differing environments, a phenomenon known as 'adaptive radiation'.

DARWIN'S FINCHES

In 1999–2000, two British biologists working at Princeton University in the USA confirmed Darwin's theories on the Galápagos finches by showing how changes in beak size in response to food supply are driven by natural selection. During drought years, when seeds are big and hard, large-beaked birds have a selective advantage and mortality is highest among small-beaked finches. DNA analysis indicated that the birds' common ancestor arrived on the islands 2–3 million years ago. The researchers also identified a gene (Bmp4) that determines beak shape and may have contributed to the divergence of these birds into distinct species.

Adapted to purpose
Darwin's own drawings of the different head and beak shapes he observed among the finches of the Galápagos Islands (above). They were first published in Zoology of the Voyage of HMS Beagle *(1840–3), a work to which other eminent naturalists such as Richard Owen and John Gould contributed.*

He confirmed his theory in 1837, after his return to England, when he began studying the series of finch-like birds that he had also collected on the Galápagos (later known as 'Darwin's finches'). The ornithologist John Gould (1804–81) identified 13 distinct species among Darwin's finch specimens, which displayed a wide variation in the shape and size of their beaks. As with the mocking birds, Darwin suspected that the birds all originated from a single ancestor, but that their geographical isolation in particular habitats had engendered different species peculiar to individual islands. Feeding specialisations led them to develop distinct beak shapes, according to whether they favoured seeds, leaves and buds, insects, or fruit.

The struggle for existence

Darwin's other stroke of genius was his theory of natural selection. He claimed that the idea first came to him while reading *An Essay on the Principle of Population* (1798) by the British political economist Thomas Malthus. Malthus contended that the rate of human population increase was outstripping the available food supply. Applying this doctrine to animals and plants, Darwin wrote in his introduction to *The Origin of Species*: 'As many more individuals of each species are born than can possibly survive, there must in every case be a struggle for existence, either one individual with another of the same species, or with the individuals of distinct species, or with the physical conditions of life. Owing to this struggle, it follows that any being, if it vary in any manner profitable to itself, under the complex and sometimes varying conditions of life, will have a better chance of survival and thus be naturally selected. From the strong principle of inheritance, any selected variety will tend to propagate its new and modified form.' This was a key point, for the spread of the 'modified form' of a particular species would result in them adapting better to their way of life. If that environment changed, or if individuals with the selective advantage migrated to other regions (as in the case of the Galápagos bird species), then natural selection might lead to the emergence of new species – a feature modern biologists call 'speciation'.

Darwin's theory in reverse
A 1901 cartoon by French illustrator Benjamin Rabier, the creator of Le Vache qui rie *(the 'Laughing Cow'), plays on the idea of the 'Descent of Man' from the apes (below). As the ape 'descends', it climbs down a gentleman in top hat and tails.*

ARTIFICIAL SELECTION

In formulating his theory of natural selection, Darwin was inspired by the process of artificial selection in animals and plants. As he wrote in *The Origin of Species*: 'The key is man's power of accumulative selection: nature gives successive variations; man adds them up in certain directions useful to him.' Here, then, the same process of selection is at work, but under human rather than nature's control, and occurring much more quickly. For this reason, 'domestic races of the same species differ from each other in the same manner as do the closely allied species of the same genus in a state of nature'. Darwin's own rearing of pigeons led him to conclude that the huge variety of breeds could not have arisen all at once but must instead have come from a single wild ancestor, the rock-pigeon (*Columba livia*).

Animal diversity
A parade of stuffed mammal species (left) on display in the 'Great Gallery of Evolution' at the Natural History Museum in Paris.

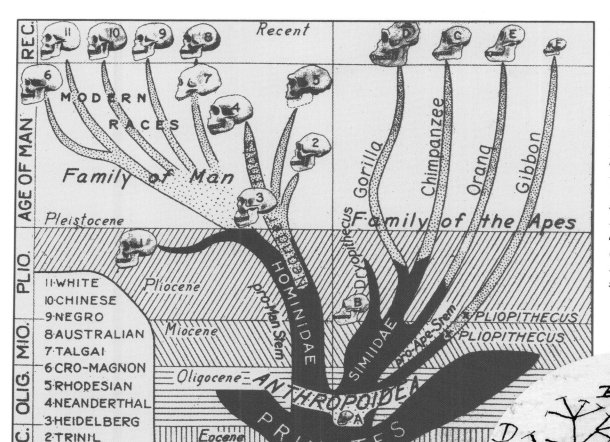

Family tree
A dendrogram of 1927 drawn by the American palaeontologist Henry Fairfield Osborn, showing the affinity between humans and the higher apes as posited by Darwin. It incorporates other 19th-century discoveries such as those of the Neanderthals (1856) and Cro-Magnon man (1868). In later years, Piltdown man was shown to be a hoax.

The tree of life

Darwin tried to represent the affinities between species in the form of a 'tree of life' diagram, or dendrogram, with various branches and twigs symbolising existing or nascent species. He emphasised the dynamic nature of this evolutionary tree: 'At each period of growth all the growing twigs have tried to branch out on all sides, and to overtop and kill the surrounding twigs and branches, in the same manner as species and groups of species have at all times overmastered other species in the great battle for life … From the first growth of the tree, many a limb and branch has decayed and dropped off; and these fallen branches of various sizes may represent those whole orders, families, and genera which have now no living representatives, and which are known to us only in a fossil state.'

Darwin's ideas caused huge debate, but were generally well received by his scientific peers. In the 20th century Darwinism, allied with Mendelian genetics, gave rise to the synthetic theory of evolution, to which most biologists now subscribe. Even so, this general orthodoxy remains open to criticism. Biologists maintain that natural selection is the sole driving force behind evolution. Yet in 1972, the palaeontologists Stephen Jay Gould and Niles Eldredge suggested that the evolution of species is not, as Darwin thought, a gradual and continuous process but rather one characterised by long periods of stasis punctuated with brief periods of rapid and major change. Likewise, the metaphor of the Tree of Life and the idea of inexorable growth and progress that underpins it – with humans, naturally, at the top of the evolutionary tree – has also been challenged. A more bush-like diagram is now preferred, with humans just one species among millions on a planet of incredible diversity.

Growth of an idea
A page from Darwin's travel notebooks of c1837, showing his first sketch of an evolutionary tree.

SOCIAL DARWINISM

The Victorian philosopher Herbert Spencer (1820–1903) used Charles Darwin's *The Origin of Species* to support his own ideas on the evolution of human societies and the concept of 'survival of the fittest' – a term coined by Spencer, not Darwin. Spencer's work gave rise to a school of thought known as 'social Darwinism'. This interpreted history as a 'struggle for existence' in which only the 'fittest' social systems survive. Social Darwinism therefore saw inequality as the driving force behind all progress.

Theoretician of evolution

A somewhat feckless student, Charles Darwin showed he had great powers of observation and analysis if a subject truly interested him. His experiences on board HMS *Beagle* (1831–6) laid the foundation of a seminal work of scholarship that cast a whole new light on the natural world.

In August 1836, HMS *Beagle* lay at anchor in Los Santos Bay on the coast of Brazil on the homeward leg of her voyage. Charles Darwin, who had first visited this place some four years earlier on the ship's outward journey, stood on deck and marvelled at the 'thousand beauties which unite all the various trees into one perfect scene'. Although he had never been much of a draughtsman, Darwin felt the urge to paint the exotic butterflies that fluttered around him and the shade cast by the 'splendid foliage' of the mango trees. Even so, no painter could have conveyed the 'ceaseless harsh music' of the cicadas. In his account of the voyage of the *Beagle*, Darwin waxed lyrical on the scene before him: 'How many times have I wished that I could find the words to express how I felt as I wandered in the shade of these magnificent forests!'

A methodical researcher

The expedition enabled Darwin to indulge a fascination for the natural world that had been with him from an early age. While aboard the *Beagle*, he followed a strict daily

Eminent scholar
A portrait of Charles Darwin (above) taken in 1868 by the celebrated British photographer Julia Margaret Cameron (1815–79), who captured many famous Victorians for posterity.

Darwin and the tortoise
An illustration of Darwin by Meredith Nugent shows him measuring the speed of a giant tortoise on the Galápagos. The drawing first appeared in the book Charles Darwin: His Life and Work *by Charles Frederick Holder, published in 1891.*

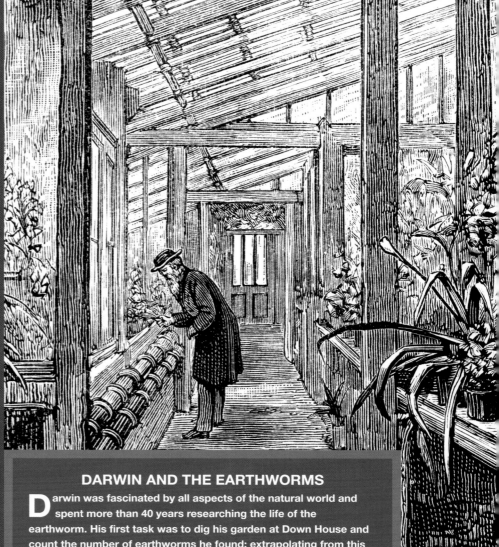

work routine that included taking notes, collecting specimens and dissecting animals. He also researched the various different peoples they would encounter on the voyage, wrote letters to relatives and friends, debated with the ship's captain, Robert FitzRoy, a fundamentalist Christian, and read avidly.

A fruitful friendship

At the age of 16 Darwin went to Edinburgh to study medicine, but found the course 'intolerably dull'. He quit medical school and instead went to Cambridge in 1827 as a first step towards a career in the clergy. Again, his studies were often neglected in favour of dinners with friends and particular interests, such as hunting and collecting species of beetle. Most importantly, he struck up a close friendship with a botany professor, John Stevens Henslow (1796–1861), who later told Darwin that Robert FitzRoy was looking for a self-funded gentleman-naturalist to join his expedition on the *Beagle*.

A love of science

After returning to England in 1836, Darwin continued with his scientific research and observations, as well as organising and augmenting his collections. He undertook an eight-year study of living and fossil cirripedes (barnacles) and also researched orchids, climbing and insectivorous plants, pollination and earthworms. From his work on the transformation of species, he formulated his famous theory of natural selection, which he finally published in 1859 as *On the Origin of Species by Means of Natural Selection*.

Looking back in his autobiography towards the end of his life, Darwin was

DARWIN AND THE EARTHWORMS

Darwin was fascinated by all aspects of the natural world and spent more than 40 years researching the life of the earthworm. His first task was to dig his garden at Down House and count the number of earthworms he found; extrapolating from this figure, he estimated that an average acre of land contained no fewer than 53,767 worms. But his most curious experiments with worms involved testing their sensory perception. Placing thousands of worms on his billiard table, Darwin blew tobacco smoke over them to see how they would react. He and his son Francis also played various instruments to the worms, including a piano, whistle and bassoon. In his last work, *The Formation of Vegetable Mould through the Action of Worms* published in 1881, he was forced to conclude that 'Worms do not possess any sense of hearing'.

Darwin at home
At Down House in Kent Darwin undertook experiments on plants in his greenhouse, resulting in numerous works including a book on orchids and a treatise on the influence of domestication on the evolution of plants.

characteristically self-deprecating about his achievements: 'With such moderate abilities as I possess, it is truly surprising that I should have influenced to a considerable extent the belief of scientific men on some important points.' He put his success down to a few key qualities: '… industry in observing and collecting facts, a fair share of invention and common sense … and the love of science.'

Enter the ironclads

The French battleship *La Gloire*, built at the naval yards at Toulon in 1859, was like no ship ever seen before. With her squat profile, vertical stern and curious superstructure, she was far removed from the sleek lines of traditional warships. From Paris, Emperor Napoleon III avidly followed the construction of his nation's revolutionary vessel.

La Gloire had the distinction of being the world's first true ironclad battleship. Her wooden hull was sheathed in armour plating 120mm thick, weighing a total of 800 tonnes. She was the brainchild of 43-year-old Henri Dupuy de Lôme, director of ship construction for the French Navy. Through the patronage of the Prince de Joinville, a naval officer who was close to Napoleon III, Dupuy de Lôme was given the task of realising the Emperor's dreams of French domination of the high seas. He was clearly the man for the job, having already constructed the world's first purpose-built steam battleship, the *Napoléon*, which had been launched in 1850.

Floating batteries

By the mid-19th century, a crucial turning point had been reached in the history of naval warfare. 'Wooden-wall' ships, with their thick timber hulls, could easily withstand the impact of cannonballs, but they were increasingly vulnerable to modern artillery firing explosive shells. At the Crimean War Battle of Sinop in November 1853, for example, the Turkish fleet had been devastated by a Russian squadron with smoothbore shell-firing cannons (Paixhans guns).

Heavily armed
A cross-sectional drawing (left) shows the gun decks of HMS Alexandra, a pre-Dreadnought British ironclad in service from 1877 to 1908. The ship was built with a double-skin hull of teak, sheathed in zinc, and was equipped with mostly muzzle-loading guns mounted in an armoured central box-battery.

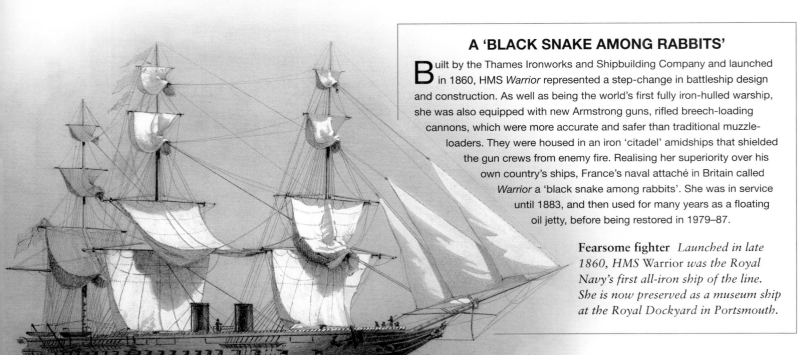

A 'BLACK SNAKE AMONG RABBITS'

Built by the Thames Ironworks and Shipbuilding Company and launched in 1860, HMS *Warrior* represented a step-change in battleship design and construction. As well as being the world's first fully iron-hulled warship, she was also equipped with new Armstrong guns, rifled breech-loading cannons, which were more accurate and safer than traditional muzzle-loaders. They were housed in an iron 'citadel' amidships that shielded the gun crews from enemy fire. Realising her superiority over his own country's ships, France's naval attaché in Britain called *Warrior* a 'black snake among rabbits'. She was in service until 1883, and then used for many years as a floating oil jetty, before being restored in 1979–87.

Fearsome fighter *Launched in late 1860, HMS* Warrior *was the Royal Navy's first all-iron ship of the line. She is now preserved as a museum ship at the Royal Dockyard in Portsmouth.*

Emperor Napoleon III of France, who had himself served as an artilleryman, took a keen interest in gunnery. In 1854 he ordered the construction of three flat-bottomed, armour-plated floating gun batteries: the *Dévastation*, the *Lave* and the *Tonnante*. They were heavy, slow (only making 4 knots) and difficult to manoeuvre – more like seaborne forts than warships. On 17 October, 1855, they were deployed against Russian shore defences at the Battle of Kinburn on the Black Sea, where they withstood barrages from the land guns and replied with salvoes of shells and cannonballs. Despite being hit 189 times, they remained afloat and the French crews sustained only two dead and 214 injured. In its first real test in battle, armour plating had acquitted itself well. Naval architects set their minds to applying this technology to fully navigable warships.

France versus Britain

The keel of *La Gloire*, which was modelled on the earlier *Napoléon*, was laid down in March 1858. She was designed to be equipped with 1,660 square metres of sail to supplement her single steam engine, giving her a top speed of just over 13 knots. The French ironclad had 36 rifled 160mm guns arranged in traditional batteries of 18 down each side. Her launch on 24 November, 1859, greatly alarmed France's old enemy, Great Britain. One contemporary commentator claimed that if she got among

CLASH OF THE TITANS

On the 8th March 1862, during the American Civil War, the Confederate ironclad CSS *Virginia* (rebuilt from the captured USS *Merrimack*) attacked five conventional frigates of the Union Navy in Hampton Roads, Virginia. The outcome was decisive: two Union vessels were sunk while the *Virginia* sustained no damage at all. The next day, the Union sent its own ironclad, the *Monitor*, into battle against the *Virginia*. The two vessels slugged it out for three hours, but neither was able to inflict telling damage on the other. This indecisive clash demonstrated the superior resilience of ironclads to wooden warships. The *Virginia* and *Monitor* also pointed the way forward in battleship design, being powered by steam alone with no rigging or sails. The *Monitor* was one of the first ships fitted with a turret equipped with two guns, which could rotate to fire in any direction without first having to manoeuvre the ship into position.

Britain's wooden-hulled fleet, it would be 'like a wolf wreaking havoc amongst sheep'.

The Admiralty responded instantly by commissioning two vessels, the *Warrior* and the *Black Prince*, which would outstrip *La Gloire* in every department. At 127 metres they were almost twice her length, and were also better armed (with 40 guns apiece) and protected (with 124mm armour plate). Most revolutionary of all, they were no longer bulky ironclad timber vessels, but sleek all-iron ships.

Scramble for supremacy

A naval race then ensued between Britain and France – soon to be joined by other nations – to outdo one another in the speed, armour and firepower of their warshps. Naval guns were made more effective through the adoption of breech-loading technology and the development of more powerful explosives.

Sea monsters
The illustration (top) shows the battle between USS Monitor *and CSS* Virginia *in Hampton Roads on 9 March 1862, the first naval engagement between ironclad warships.*

First of many
HMS Dreadnought *(below) photographed shortly after her launch in 1906. She gave her name to a whole generation of capital ships, but missed the Battle of Jutland as she was undergoing a refit.* Dreadnought *was sold for scrap in 1922, and broken up at Inverness the following year.*

Famous battleship
A Soviet poster (above) for Battleship Potemkin, *directed by Sergei Eisenstein in 1925. The film recounts an anti-tsarist mutiny that took place on board* Potemkin *at the Black Sea port of Odessa in 1905, an event that foreshadowed the Russian Revolution of October 1917.*

One key advance was the invention of Palliser shot, a prototype armour-piercing shell, in 1867. In response, armour plate became even thicker. But just as it was becoming unfeasibly heavy, advances in metallurgy made it possible to produce much lighter steel plates – only some 300mm thick – that were even more resistant than iron. The manufacture of all-steel armour was pioneered by the French Schneider steelworks in Le Creusot.

By the end of the 19th century, navies had abandoned sail rigging in favour of all-steam propulsion. At the same time, the number of guns was reduced, with heavier-calibre artillery being mounted in turrets that could swivel in all directions. In 1906, the launch of the British battleship HMS *Dreadnought* marked another seminal moment in the warship development. She was powered by revolutionary steam turbines that gave her a top speed of 25 knots, while her ten 12-inch guns made her the world's first 'all-big-gun' ship. So great was her impact that she gave her name to an entire generation of battleships. Navies around the world frantically re-equipped.

By around 1910, Britain, France and Germany were caught up in a race to acquire ever more powerful battleships. So much capital was invested that when the First World War began in 1914 none of the combatants wanted to risk their fleets in an all-out battle. The only significant engagement of the war was the Battle of Jutland between the British and German navies in 1916; Britain lost more ships and men, but retained control of the North Sea. The conflict emphasised the vulnerability of huge battleships to smaller weapons systems like submarines and mines.

Decline of the battleship

By the 1920s, the development of naval air power and aircraft carriers signalled the beginning of the end for battleships. Hugely expensive to build, they were sitting ducks for torpedos and dive-bombers. In the Second World War, the major powers all refitted older battleships and launched new ones, but they were mainly used to support carrier operations, especially in the Pacific conflict between Japan and the USA. By the end of hostilities, it was clear that the ironclads' heirs were obsolescent. Britain's last battleship, HMS *Vanguard*, was launched in 1944 and decommissioned in 1960.

AN INCONCLUSIVE BATTLE

The British Grand Fleet and the German High Seas Fleet clashed off Denmark's Jutland peninsula on 31 May, 1916. More than 250 ships of all types took part in what was the only major naval battle of the First World War. Despite British numerical superiority, with 28 dreadnought-class battleships to 16 on the German side, the outcome was indecisive. Superior gunnery enabled the German commander, Admiral Reinhard Scheer, to sink two of Admiral David Beatty's battlecruisers, the *Indefatigable* and the *Queen Mary*. The arrival of the main British fleet under Admiral John Jellicoe turned the tide, but a daring manoeuvre by Scheer saw most of his ships reach port under cover of night. Final losses were heavy, with 14 British and 11 German ships sunk, killing 6,094 British and 2,550 Germans. Both sides claimed victory, but Germany never again risked her surface fleet in open battle, concentrating instead on submarine warfare. The British enjoyed continued mastery of the North Sea.

Jellicoe's fighting ships *An oil painting of 1916 by Montague Dawson shows the British Grand Fleet in action at Jutland.*

Awesome firepower
Aside from museum pieces, the only battleship to survive into the 21st century is the 45,000-ton USS Iowa. Mothballed by the US government, it is maintained ready to re-enter service should an international crisis arise.

A new source of power

The Belgian engineer Étienne Lenoir invented an engine that would soon make steam obsolete. Compact, light and powerful, the new engine ushered in an age of greater mechanisation and mobility, exemplified by the growth of the automobile industry.

Shape of the future
Lenoir's original engine (right), which went into production in 1860. At its height, Lenoir's company was turning out almost 400 engines a year. Manufacture of the Lenoir gas engine in England was licensed to the Reading Gas Works in 1865.

Hissing, whistling and filling the air of mills and factories with a warm mist, steam engines had increased industrial output tenfold by the end of the 18th century. Yet while such engines could generate considerable power, they were also heavy, cumbersome and dangerous. There were many instances of catastrophic boiler explosions sinking steamships or destroying factories. And although steam engines could meet the demands of heavy industry, they were less well suited to lighter or more intermittent use required by smaller workshops.

Steam carriages, which began to appear from the early 19th century, suffered from the same shortcomings. The few people who owned these spluttering, ponderous machines were forced to make frequent stops in order to top up the boiler – which could weigh anything between 1.8 and 8 tonnes – or to stoke the fire. A safer alternative had been available since around 1816 in the form of hot-air engines, in which the pistons were driven by the expansion of air within the cylinders, but these were expensive, consumed a lot of energy and delivered insufficient power.

THE LENOIR ENGINE

Étienne Lenoir put the finishing touches to his engine in 1859, before demonstrating it for the first time in January 1860 to a group of 20 specially invited guests. The proud inventor turned a gas-tap, pressed the ignition and the engine burst into life amid a great round of applause. The heavy flywheel on the prototype turned at a rate of 30 revolutions per minute. It was driven by a piston that moved back and forth horizontally. Two pairs of brass slide valves admitted the fuel–air mixture and discharged the exhaust gases, while a centrifugal flyball governor controlled the engine's speed of rotation.

HOT-AIR ENGINES

The precursor of the Lenoir engine was the hot-air or 'caloric' engine. This comprised a cylinder continually heated by an external source of combustion. The air within the cylinder expanded, driving two pistons that served both to impart motion and to circulate air between the hot and cold parts of the system. Although caloric engines were complicated and expensive to make, they were reliable, quiet, easy to use and, above all, had no need for an internal boiler. But they could only generate around 2 horsepower. The Scottish pastor Robert Stirling lent his name to an engine operating on the hot-air principle, which he patented in 1817. Stirling engines were extremely popular in small-scale operations, such as light engineering or pumping out wells.

Internal combustion

To increase the efficiency of engines, engineers came up with the idea of creating combustion within the engine itself, by utilising the flammability of the oxygen contained in air. But there was still the problem of what fuel to use: wood and coal were unsuitable, as they left a deposit that clogged up the cylinders. By contrast, coal gas, which began to be produced in France and England from around 1815 onwards, was easy to get hold of, cheap and produced no ash or soot when burned.

The first practical internal combustion engine appeared in 1859, the brainchild of the Belgian engineer Étienne Lenoir. This single-cylinder, two-stroke engine was an

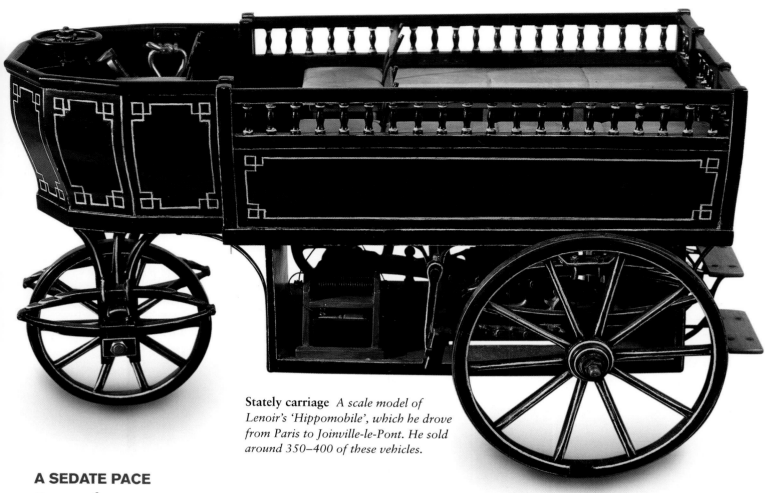

Stately carriage *A scale model of Lenoir's 'Hippomobile', which he drove from Paris to Joinville-le-Pont. He sold around 350–400 of these vehicles.*

A SEDATE PACE

In 1863 Étienne Lenoir built a four-stroke engine based on principles outlined by Alphonse Beau de Rochas. The same year he fitted this motor onto a three-wheeled carriage, which he drove from Paris to Joinville-le-Pont and back – a distance of 12 miles – in three hours.

instant success, especially in light engineering. Its electric ignition fired it up straight away, compared to the minute-and-a-half minimum that it took to get a steam engine going. But almost as quickly, the honeymoon period was over: in sustained use, the engine gave off such a fierce heat that it required an unwieldy water-cooling system to stop it overheating. Lenoir sold only a few hundred engines, most of which soon ended up on the scrapheap, replaced by the very steam engines they were supposed to supplant.

Lenoir's colleague and friend, the French engineer Alphonse Beau de Rochas, worked out a four-stroke combustion cycle that generated greater power by compressing the fuel–air mixture before exploding it. He filed a patent in 1862 and the next year Lenoir found a practical application for the idea.

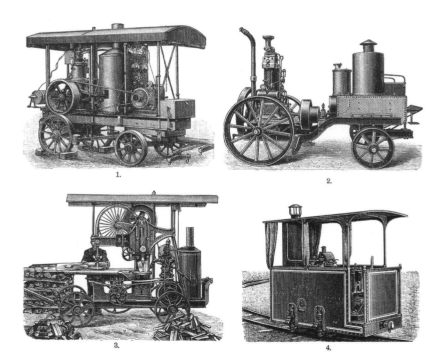

Gas engines *Early internal combustion engines were used to power various pieces of farm equipment, like these reproduced from a plate in a German encyclopedia of 1895, the* Brockhaus Konversations-Lexikon.

A BORN INVENTOR

Étienne Lenoir came from a Belgian farming family but left home at the age of 16 to work in Paris for an enameller and electroplater. Entirely self-taught, he soon showed an aptitude for invention, devising a method of whitening enamel and filing his first patent in 1847 at the age of 25. He spent much of his free time at the Museum of Arts and Crafts in Paris, attending a course of lectures on engineering and studying the collections. It was there that he met the engineer Alphonse Beau de Rochas. Between 1855 and 1857, Lenoir invented and patented many pieces of electrical apparatus, including braking systems, railway signals, an electric dough-kneading machine for bakeries, a regulator for dynamos and water meters. To manufacture and market his 1859 coal-gas engine, he founded the Lenoir–Gautier Engine Company in Paris; the first production model, generating 4 horsepower, was operating in a master turner's workshop by May 1860. Later on, Lenoir won fame and fortune for devising an improved electrical telegraph, which could transmit both written messages and drawings. The system was widely used during the Prussian siege of Paris in 1870. He also developed new processes for silvering mirrors and tanning leather. By the time of his death in 1900, Lenoir had filed no fewer than 75 patents.

The Otto engine

Five years later, the German inventor Nikolaus Otto, who had followed Lenoir's work with interest, began building an 'atmospheric gas engine', so called because the downward stroke of the piston was provided by gravity and atmospheric pressure. Compressing the coal gas before it was ignited generated twice the power of Lenoir's engine while using only half the fuel. Otto's work was funded by a wealthy entrepreneur named Eugen Langen, and the resulting Langen–Otto two-stroke engine won the gold medal at the Paris Exhibition of 1867. Otto went on to perfect his engine in 1876 with the help of the engineers Gottlieb Daimler and Wilhelm Maybach. Known as the 'Otto Silent' (his 1867 engine was very noisy), this new engine worked on a four-stroke cycle.

To adapt this light and powerful engine to fit an automobile, Otto tried switching the fuel from flammable gas to a flammable liquid.

Speedy roadster *In 1895, Farnham inventor John Henry Knight designed and built this petrol-driven vehicle, which had a top speed of 12mph. No sooner had he taken it out for a test drive than he was stopped and charged with 'using a locomotive without a licence' and not having a man walk in front with a red flag.*

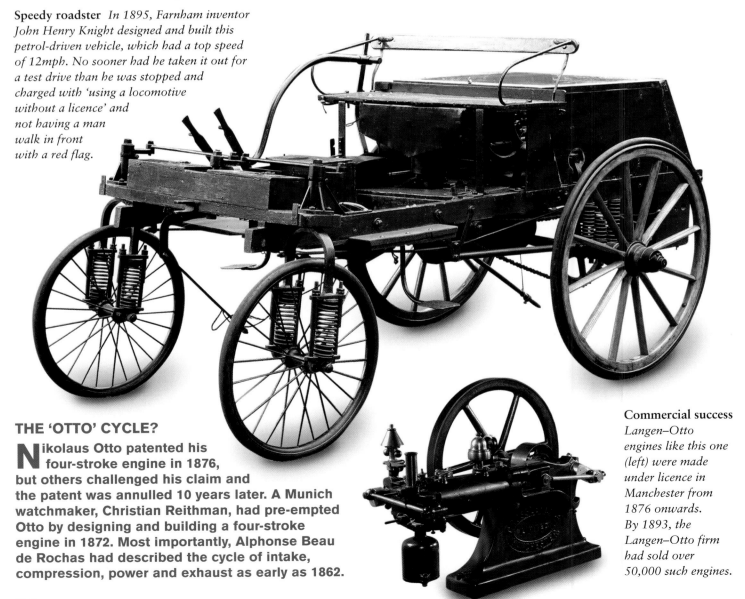

THE 'OTTO' CYCLE?

Nikolaus Otto patented his four-stroke engine in 1876, but others challenged his claim and the patent was annulled 10 years later. A Munich watchmaker, Christian Reithman, had pre-empted Otto by designing and building a four-stroke engine in 1872. Most importantly, Alphonse Beau de Rochas had described the cycle of intake, compression, power and exhaust as early as 1862.

Commercial success *Langen–Otto engines like this one (left) were made under licence in Manchester from 1876 onwards. By 1893, the Langen–Otto firm had sold over 50,000 such engines.*

He experimented unsuccessfully with rock-oil, phenol and alcohol before lighting on petroleum as the ideal fuel. He began installing the 'Otto Silent' in cars and in farm engines from the mid-1880s onwards. Agricultural output was boosted by the use of these machines. Yields increased hugely, while the demand for manpower was much reduced, further contributing to the ongoing exodus from the countryside to the city.

THE FOUR-STROKE CYCLE

The engine cycle first described by Alphonse Beau de Rochas comprises four stages. The first of these is intake (1) in which the piston descends, drawing a mixture of air and fuel (coal gas in early engines, later petrol) into the cylinder through an inlet valve. As the piston rises in what is called the compression stroke (2) the air, trapped by the closing of the inlet valve, is compressed at the top of the cylinder. A spark plug then ignites the fuel-air mixture. The expanding hot gases force the piston down through the power stroke (3). On the final exhaust stroke (4), the exhaust valve opens to allow the products of combustion to escape from the cylinder.

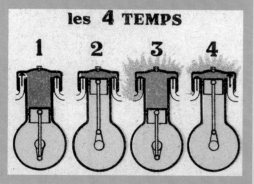

les 4 TEMPS

Four-stroke engines became the power plant of choice for virtually all new automobiles and boats; a study conducted in England in 1897 counted over 400 different types in operation. Marine versions were widely used in patrol craft and motor torpedo boats during the First World War.

Ultimately, the internal combustion engine would be refined and perfected by German pioneers of the automobile industry such as Karl Benz, Gottlieb Daimler and Rudolf Diesel. By the late 19th century, sufficiently powerful and reliable engines had been developed to make motor vehicles a viable proposition. The demand for fuel boosted the oil industry. Soon oil was considered a key energy resource, every bit as important as coal.

No spark
Rudolf Diesel and colleagues pictured in 1893 in the factory in Augsburg where he developed a new type of internal combustion engine. Unlike the petrol engine, Diesel's invention required no spark plug, but rather ignited the fuel by the heat of compression alone. This highly efficient engine would eventually be named after him.

Cutting edge *Engine manufacturers use Formula One motor racing as a testbed for research and development. Pictured here is the British driver Lewis Hamilton in a McLaren car, powered by a Mercedes-Benz engine, winning the Japanese Grand Prix in September 2007.*

Internal combustion engine

Inventions seldom appear out of the blue, fully fledged. Almost invariably, they build on a sequence of earlier developments. The internal combustion engine – the natural successor to the steam engine – would revolutionise transport, making the automobile and aeroplane possible.

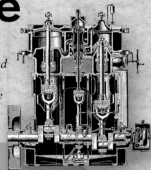

Movement is transferred from the piston to the connecting rods, thence to the crankshaft.

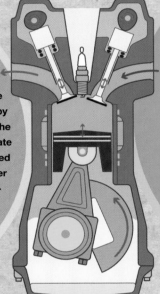

INTAKE
THE CAMSHAFT AND VALVE

When the inlet valves are open, they let the fuel-air mixture into the cylinders. When closed, they seal the combustion chamber at the moment of ignition in order to produce the highest performance. The valves open and close at precise intervals determined by the motion of the camshaft, which in turn is regulated by the crankshaft. The concept of the valve goes back to the late 2nd century BC and Ctesibius of Alexandria, who devised an ingenious method of keeping the water flow in water clocks at a constant rate. This comprised a teardrop-shaped wooden float bobbing on the water in the inflow vessel; as the water level rose, the float moved up into the inlet pipe, thus slowing down the flow from the reservoir.

MOTIVE POWER
PISTON, CONNECTING ROD AND CRANKSHAFT

The internal combustion engine uses the simple principle that gas expands when heated. Because the gas is in an enclosed space (the cylinder), as it expands with the heat it increases the pressure in the cylinder, driving down the piston. Once the pressure is released by the explosion, the piston naturally rises again. Like valves, the idea of the cylinder comes from Ctesibius, the 'father of pneumatics'. The Arab engineer and scholar al-Jazary built a two-cylinder pump in the 13th century to draw water from wells. The up-and-down motion of the pistons is transmitted by a connecting rod to a crankshaft, which transforms linear movement into continuous rotary motion. Crankshafts have been in use in hydraulic engines since the Middle Ages for beating metal, tanning leather or crushing hemp seeds.

IGNITION
WITH AND WITHOUT SPARK PLUGS

When the fuel-air mixture reaches the required compression level, it is ignited by a spark, creating the explosion that forces down the piston. The spark is produced by a spark plug, the direct descendant of the 'pistol' invented by Italian physicist Alessandro Volta in 1766, comprising a bottle filled with an explosive mixture of hydrogen and oxygen and sealed with a cork. An electrode in the bottle produced a spark that ignited the gases, blowing out the stopper. In 1775 Swiss inventor François de Rivaz built a primitive internal combustion engine powered by hydrogen and oxygen. But it was Étienne Lenoir who, in 1876, incorporated the first true ancestor of the modern spark plug into his gas engine. Spark plugs played no part in the engine designed by Rudolf Diesel in 1893, which used a higher compression ratio to initiate ignition.

Volta's 'pistol' (above) and a modern spark plug (right).

The diagram above shows the workings of an internal combustion engine: the spark plug (top centre) is flanked by the inlet and exhaust valves; below them, the piston rises and falls within the cylinder, driving the connecting rod (bottom), which generates the engine's continuous rotary movement.

TRANSMISSION
UNIVERSAL JOINT AND GEARS

Transmission of the rotary motion of the crankshaft into the transverse rotation that drives the wheels of a car is achieved by the so-called 'universal joint'. Originally devised by the 16th-century Italian mathematician Girolamo Cardano, it was reinvented by the British scientist Robert Hooke in 1676. The gearbox, which is operated by a clutch pedal, ensures that the car can bring optimal traction to bear in all conditions. Gears are just one application of an invention that dates back some 2,500 years – the cogwheel, which has been used in clocks and countless other mechanisms.

THE CARBURETTOR
DIRECT OR INDIRECT INJECTION

The carburettor, the device that creates the fuel-air mixture, was patented by Karl Benz in 1886. Seven years later, the German designer Wilhelm Maybach developed the float-feed carburettor, which vaporises the fuel through a jet as a fine spray. In direct injection engines, only air is taken into the cylinder in the first phase of the cycle; fuel is then injected directly into the combustion chamber. This helps to reduce fuel consumption when the engine is just ticking over, for example, when sitting in traffic jams. In indirect injection engines, fuel is injected into an intake port behind the intake valve. The system is cheaper but produces higher emissions and less power.

FUEL
FROM PETROL TO BIOFUELS

Bitumen, the tar-like, raw substance from which petroleum is refined, has been used since late antiquity as a building material or to waterproof the hulls of boats. Distilled in the form of naphtha, it became popular as a lamp fuel. From the 1880s onwards, refined petrol established itself as the optimal fuel for internal combustion engines. Another of the fuels that has been derived from oil since the late 19th century is gas-oil, or diesel. Since the late 20th century, concerns about dwindling oil supplies and the environmental damage caused by burning fossil fuels have shifted the focus onto developing biofuels distilled from plant crops.

The production of biofuels from specially grown crops is one proposed solution to future oil shortages and the environmental impact of burning fossil fuels.

A Maybach engine (above), built in 1922 to power the Zeppelin airship LZ126.

Charlie Chaplin's view of cogwheels and gears in his 1936 film Modern Times *(left).*

THE FUTURE
ALTERNATIVE AND FUTURE ENGINES

The rotary engine, developed by the German engineer Felix Wankel in the 1950s, has no valves, connecting rods or crankshaft. Instead of pistons, it uses a triangular rotor spinning inside a 'cylinder' shaped like a fat figure of eight; the geometry of the rotor and cylinder effectively creates three separate combustion chambers. Rotary engines vibrate less than conventional engines, but they burn more fuel. The Japanese car manufacturer Mazda has spearheaded their development since 1978. In Stirling engines, combustion is external. A fixed volume of gas such as air or helium circulates through the cylinders in a closed circuit. The cycle consists of compressing the gas while cool, heating it, expanding the hot gas, then cooling it once more before the cycle begins again. Latterly, engine manufacturers have begun to put economy before power, leading to cleaner and more fuel-efficient engines. Future car development is focusing on hybrid vehicles that combine internal combustion power with electric power.

A Wankel rotary engine (right) of the type installed in the Citroën GS car in 1973.

The Yale cylinder lock 1860

The ancient Egyptians invented the dowel-pin lock in c1500 BC. This comprised a bolt set into two surface mounts that were entirely enclosed except for a small opening for the key. Moveable dowels dropped into recesses ('mortices') on the bolt and locked the door. As the key was inserted, it pushed the dowel-pins ('tumblers') up, so allowing the bolt to be removed and the door to open.

The lock underwent few changes in the centuries that followed, except for the addition of 'wards' – metal projections inside the lock shaped to match the notches on the key. The

Master craftsman
An ornate Bramah lock of 1787. Other inventions by this prolific British inventor include a version of the flushing toilet, an hydraulic press, and a machine for automatically numbering banknotes.

THROWING DOWN THE GAUNTLET

So confident was Joseph Bramah in the security of his lock that in 1790 he placed an example in the window of his shop with a sign that read: 'The Artist who can make an Instrument that will unpick or open this Lock shall Receive 200 Guineas the Moment it is produced.' The lock withstood all attempts until the Great Exhibition of 1851, when an American, Alfred Hobbs, finally succeeded after 24 days of trying.

lever or 'bit-key' lock was introduced later. This involved levers with different teeth cut to specific levels; when the correct key was inserted, the levers would align, allowing the key to continue on until it threw the latch.

Tumblers, cylinders and springs

In 1778 the English locksmith Robert Barron developed the tumbler lock, a refinement of the lever lock, in which each one of a series (up to six in the most secure versions) of lever tumblers was activated by a separate step of the key. In 1784 Joseph Bramah patented the cylinder lock, in which only an exact alignment of the lock edges with corresponding grooves on the barrel of the key (which Bramah made of different heights) enabled the key to turn. In 1817 the Portsmouth Royal Dockyard was burgled and the British government offered a

Key innovation
Bramah's original cylinder lock of 1784 (left) was manufactured by his apprentice Henry Maudslay, who went on to become famous as the inventor of the machine tool.

Famous name
A Yale lock and key (right) made by the Yale Lock Manufacturing Company, founded in 1868 by Linus Yale and Henry R Towne.

reward for an unpickable lock. In response, Jeremiah Chubb introduced his 'detector' lock, so called because it incorporated a mechanism that effectively disabled it if tampered with. In the 1850s, the American Robert Newell introduced removable tumblers that could be disassembled and scrambled, and keys with interchangeable 'bits' (the notched end part that engages with the lock).

Security at last

The modern door key was developed in 1860 by the American engineer Linus Yale. A major innovation was that the serrations ran the entire length of the key. It was inserted into a slot cut in the centre of a plug that rotated within the cylinder and the notches on the key lifted five or six spring-loaded pins. The pins were made in two halves of unequal lengths – if any of the crests and valleys on the key failed to match the pin, the lock would not turn. The notches on these small, flat keys could be cut in an infinite variety of patterns.

Combination locks provided greater protection for strong-boxes and safes. Latterly, though, keys have been superseded by magnetic locks and digital keycards, notably in banks and hotels.

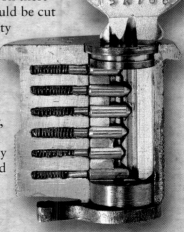

The dentist's drill 1863

In 1865 George Fellows Harrington presented his invention to the Odontological Society of Great Britain as an apparatus suitable for 'drilling, cutting, grinding and polishing teeth while in the mouth'. By then Harrington had already been using his device, the world's first mechanical dentist's drill, in his own practice for two years. Prior to this, dentists used small hand-driven drills manipulated between the index finger and thumb. This was such a long and painful operation that patients usually opted for tooth extraction rather than repair. Harrington's drill was very noisy, but this was soon overcome by means of a pneumatic drive operated by the foot. The first electric dental drill was patented in 1870.

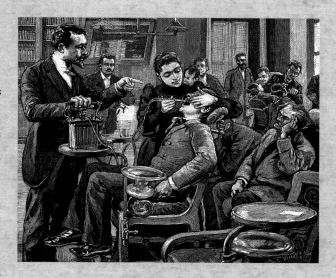

Open wide
Harrington's original dental drill ran on clockwork; it was wound up with a large key and ran for two minutes at a time. The machine sold for six guineas. Harrington named his device Erado (Latin for 'I scrape out').

The pneumatic drill 1861

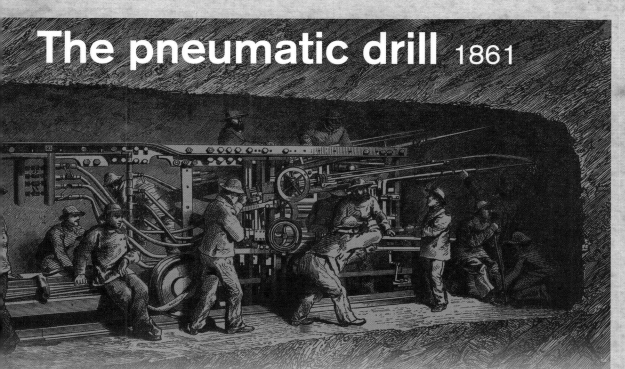

At the rockface
Sommeiller's pneumatic drill at work, boring the Mont Cénis tunnel 1,600m beneath the Alps. The French and Italian excavation teams, who began tunnelling from either side of the mountain, met up in December 1870.

The pneumatic drill was invented during the excavation of the Mont Cénis (or Fréjus) railway tunnel, the first tunnel to link France and Italy under the Alps. Work got underway in 1857 using traditional tunnelling techniques, with workers hacking out holes with crowbars and filling them with gunpowder, but progress was painfully slow through the hard granite. In an attempt to speed things up, in 1861 the French engineer in charge of the project, Germain Sommeiller, developed a pneumatic drill that ran on compressed air. He had got the idea from steam-driven drills that he saw working in British coal mines. Sommeiller cleverly utilised hydraulic power; a 30-metre pipe ran from a waterfall at the mouth of the tunnel to power a compressor, which forced air down cast-iron pipes to the drilling machine at the rockface. The tunnelling rate increased dramatically, from 0.75 metres to 2.44 metres a day. The tunnel opened to traffic on 19 September, 1871.

THE MACHINE GUN – 1862
Mechanised killing

Montigny mitrailleuse
On this early type of machine gun, a magazine of 37 cartridges was inserted into the breech and all 37 shots were fired at once.

Warfare changed for ever with the invention of the machine gun in 1862. Individual soldiers could now unleash a withering hail of fire that before would have taken dozens, or even hundreds, of riflemen to produce. The carnage on the battlefields of the First World War testified to the murderous efficacy of the new weapon.

Rapid fire
Royal Navy sailors manning a Gatling gun, c1878. The Gatling was heavy and difficult to manoeuvre during firing.

HUMANIST OR WARMONGER?

In 1877 Richard Gatling claimed that humanitarian considerations had driven him to invent his machine gun. Having seen the suffering of Union soldiers laid low by dysentery and malaria in the American Civil War, he wanted to devise a weapon that would reduce the size of armies and bring conflicts to a swift end. But on 18 February, 1864, in a letter to Abraham Lincoln while the conflict still raged, he made no secret of his desire to 'crush the rebellion'.

In 1862, just after the outbreak of the American Civil War, Dr Richard J Gatling patented a radical new gun bearing his name. Mounted on a two-wheeled carriage, the weapon had six barrels rotated by a hand crank; the cartridges were held in a hopper above and fell into place by gravity-feed. The idea behind the six revolving barrels was that each had time to cool before it came back into the firing position. This rapid-fire gun could discharge several hundred rounds a minute.

The idea was not new: as early as the 2nd century AD, the Chinese had constructed repeating crossbows. In 1718 an English lawyer named James Puckle designed a large-calibre tripod-mounted flintlock intended for use on board ships to repel boarders. The so-called 'Defence Gun' had a single barrel fed by a revolving cylinder with 11 chambers, and could discharge 63 shots in seven minutes. A prototype was built and demonstrated, but it never made it into mass production.

The 19th century saw several unsatisfactory attempts at a machine gun. A prime example was the 'mitrailleuse' developed by the Belgian Joseph Montigny from 1859 onwards, an improved version of the 1851 volley gun invented by his compatriot, Toussaint-Henry-Joseph Fafchamps. The Montigny mitrailleuse originally fired 37 simultaneous shots, but was later fitted with a cam wheel that enabled it to fire one shot at a time.

International hit

The Gatling gun was first deployed during the American Civil War at the Battle of Petersburg in 1864. It was also fitted onto some of the Union ships. Various other repeating guns – the Vandenberg, the Rega, the Agar and the

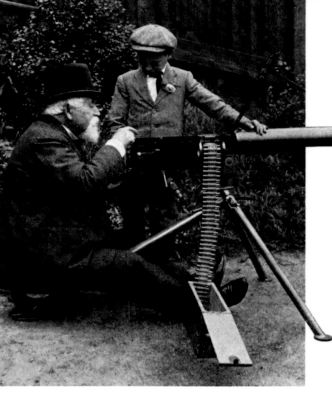

copies of the Maxim – the MG1908 and the Pulemyot Maxima PM1910 respectively.

Industrialised warfare

The military advantages of the machine gun were clear. Britain's campaigns in southern Africa, from 1893 onwards, had shown that just a handful of troops firing Maxim guns could hold off thousands of tribesmen. Now, with Europe on the brink of conflict, the rival nations rushed to rearm and warfare entered the industrial age. The withering firepower of machine guns brought about a fundamental change in tactics; when one such gun could mow down entire regiments, charges by cavalry or mass infantry were nothing short of suicidal, and trench warfare became the order of the day. A whole new range of machine guns entered service during the First World War: the Vickers Gun (an improved Maxim gun; 1912), the Lewis gun or Lewis Automatic Machine Rifle, a light machine gun (1915), the Browning (1917) and the German Gast gun (1916). As the war progressed, these weapons were mounted on armoured cars, tanks and aeroplanes.

Not a toy
Hiram Maxim demonstrates his machine gun to his grandson in 1893. Maxim was a prolific inventor interested not only in arms but also in powered flight; he designed several unsuccessful flying machines.

Personal firepower
All armies are now equipped with assault rifles that can be used as fully automatic or single-shot weapons. The soldier (below), with a Kalashnikov AK-47, is an Iranian in the Iran-Iraq War of 1980-8.

Williams guns – were also field-tested during the conflict, but all were found wanting. The US army officially adopted an improved version of the Gatling gun in 1866.

In 1884 another American, Hiram Maxim, developed the world's first fully automatic machine gun. The Maxim gun had a single barrel cooled by a water-filled sleeve, and it utilised the energy of the fired projectile's recoil to eject the spent cartridge case and reload the weapon. Fed by a flexible belt of cartridges, it kept up a continuous stream of fire at a rate of 600 rounds a minute for as long as the operator kept pressing the trigger. The US Army purchased it in 1889, and other countries soon followed suit. Imperial Germany and Russia manufactured their own

DEVELOPMENT OF THE SUBMACHINE GUN

Early machine guns were heavy and unwieldy, requiring a team of operators, and were unsuitable for fast-moving or close-quarter combat. Portable automatic weapons firing revolver-calibre cartridges began to appear towards the end of the First World War. The first true submachine gun was the MP18, invented by Germans Louis Schmeisser and Theodor Bergmann, which came too late to change the outcome of the war. It was soon imitated, notably, from 1919, by the American John T Thompson. The 'Tommy gun' became the favoured weapon of 1920s gangsters. At the end of the Second World War, the Germans introduced the Sturmgewehr 44, which fired rifle rounds. This was the world's first true assault rifle and it served as the model for the most famous weapon of them all, the AK-47, designed by the Russian Mikhail Kalashnikov.

Age of the train

The building of the railways – with all the incumbent infrastructure of tracks, stations, bridges, tunnels and viaducts – involved huge feats of civil engineering. The driving forces behind the rapid creation of this new transport network were technological innovation and commercial enterprise. Almost overnight, the railways transformed national economies, landscapes and the way that people lived.

Blasting a way through

Creating the Olive Mount Cutting (below) was one of the biggest engineering feats involved in constructing the Liverpool to Manchester line. The sandstone was blasted and excavated to make a cutting 6m wide, 25m deep and almost 3,000m long. Rock from the cutting was used to build the Sankey Viaduct on the same line.

The railway came to epitomise the sheer energy and dynamism of the 19th century and the dramatic change of pace that industrialisation brought to people's lives. Henry Booth, treasurer of the Liverpool and Manchester Railway (the world's first intercity passenger line, opened in 1830), clearly understood the profound changes the line brought about: 'Perhaps the most striking result produced by the completion of this railway is the sudden change which has been effected in our ideas of time and space. What was quick is now slow; what was distant is now near; and this realisation of our ideas will permeate the whole of society.'

Full steam ahead

The railway became the catalyst for ongoing technological and social progress. Not only did it stimulate advances in steam engines, iron and steel manufacture and coal mining, but as railway networks spread they prompted a hitherto unimagined growth in the circulation of goods and people. Railway timetables even changed the perception of time, as local time was replaced by unified railway time – Reading, for example, 30 miles west of London, had traditionally been 10 minutes behind the capital. Insular, agrarian societies suddenly gained a window on the world.

The dawn of a new age was evident at the Rainhill locomotive trials in 1829, when George Stephenson's *Rocket* triumphed over rival steam locomotives and also over an engine, the *Cycloped*, powered by a horse on a treadmill. This symbolised the move away from a thousand years and more of animal traction. The performance of early locomotives

Railway pioneer

A coloured wood engraving – from an 1870 painting by Ludwig Burger – shows a top-hatted George Stephenson overseeing work on the Liverpool and Manchester Railway. The opening ceremony took place on 15 September, 1830, but was marred by tragedy when the Member of Parliament for Liverpool got down on the track and was struck and killed by Stephenson's Rocket.

...ay seem unimpressive by modern standards, ...t the increase from the 8mph of a trotting ...orse to 25–30mph by train was a quantum ...ap. In less than a century, for instance, ...e journey time from London to Bristol came ...own from 20 hours to just 5½. Early train ...avel was far from comfortable – passengers ...d to brave steam, smoke, smuts, embers, ...stling crowds and stuffy, claustrophobic ...rriages. But for all that, the railway ...creased people's mobility and made remote ...gions and towns accessible.

Major upheaval

The railway was by no means universally welcomed. Many people found the clanking, fire-breathing steam engines terrifying. Many landowners refused to let the railway cross their property, and railway entrepreneurs were often regarded as fraudsters – an impression compounded by several financial scandals arising from railway speculation.

The first railway lines in England were built over difficult, hilly terrain in the north of the country. Their construction entailed huge

Study in steam
The Gare Saint-Lazare in Paris, opened in 1837, became the subject of a series of pictures by the Impressionist painter Claude Monet. This canvas, Le Pont de l'Europe (1877) in now in the city's Marmottan Museum.

THE RAILWAY KING

In 1827 George Hudson, a draper from York, received a sudden windfall when a great-uncle left him £30,000 in his will. Spotting a financial opportunity in the growing railway business, Hudson bought 500 shares in the new Leeds to York line. Success followed success, and Hudson soon gained a reputation for high living. He proved to be a master at mergers and the acquisition of failing companies, and in exploiting rights of way. In 1844 he formed the Midland Railway, which ran trains to London, and the North British Railway for services to

Scotland. His election as an MP in 1846 helped him to expand his business empire even further. But evidence of fraud emerged and Hudson was tried and convicted of false accounting, misappropriation of funds and bribery. The 'Railway King' was jailed in 1865 and died a pauper in 1871.

Midland Railway crest
The Midland slogan was 'The best route for comfortable travel, fine scenery and a restaurant service'.

No obstacle
Taking the railway across Deepdale Beck, Co. Durham, in 1858. Designed by Thomas Bouch, the viaduct was supported by 50m-high cast-iron pillars.

The United Kingdom was the proving ground for all subsequent railway ventures, and between 1830 and 1900 it maintained a workforce of some 50,000 navvies. Fatalities were frequent. Some structures, like curving viaducts or long tunnels, posed new civil engineering problems. In a world that was still without the telephone or telegraph, railway entrepreneurs like the Stephensons and Thomas Brassey achieved astonishing results, constructing projects not just in their native Britain but around the world. When he died in 1870, Brassey had built one in every 20 miles of railway that then existed worldwide.

The golden age of railway building

The years 1840–90 were the heyday of railway building and many nations rushed to follow Britain's lead. In 1835 Belgium and Germany became the first European countries to establish a railway system, followed by Russia in 1837 and France in 1842. Before long, the length of a nation's rail network became a yardstick for its international standing. Technological advances helped to improve all aspects of rail travel, from the efficiency of engines and the comfort of passenger coaches to the safety of signalling and lighting. Magnificent mainline terminus stations such as London's St Pancras (1877), New York's Grand Central Station (*c*1900) and the Gare de Lyon in Paris (1901) sprang up in a variety of architectural styles, like monumental cathedrals of the industrial age.

The huge enterprise of railway construction by private companies was supported by an equally impressive system of finance. The investment and ambitious engineering works, as tunnels were dug, viaducts erected and the landscape scarred by embankments and cuttings. All this activity and change unsettled public opinion, as documented by the Victorian writers Elizabeth Gaskell and Anthony Trollope in their novels *Cranford* (1851) and *The Way We Live Now* (1875).

SPANNING THE USA

The first railway line in America ran from Baltimore to Ellicot's Mills and was opened on 24 May, 1830. For many years, railroads in the United States remained regional enterprises, but in 1869 the Union Pacific Railroad, building westward from Omaha, joined with the Central Pacific Railroad to form the first transcontinental link. Work on the line began after the American Civil War (1861–5) and was hailed as a great act of national reconciliation, with ex-soldiers from both sides working side-by-side. The two teams met at Promontory Point in Utah on 10 May, 1869, creating a through line from Chicago to San Francisco. In 1881 a second transcontinental link was completed with the joining of the Atchison, Topeka and Santa Fe Railway to the South Pacific Railroad.

Transcontinental Railroad *Navvies and a locomotive fitted with a 'cowcatcher' at Green River, Wyoming, in 1866.*

THE TRANS-SIBERIAN RAILWAY

The plan for a railway line from Tomsk to Vladivostok via Irkutsk was first mooted in 1885–6 by Count Ignatieff and Baron Korff. Nine years later, under the presidency of the newly crowned Tsar Nicholas II, one-quarter of the Trans-Siberian Railway had been completed. Construction of the remainder of the line was slowed by various factors: slapdash workmanship (political prisoners were used as labourers), poor quality materials, the severe climate and widespread corruption. The through line from Moscow to Vladivostok was finally completed in 1900. Trains left every Saturday evening (it did not become a daily service until 1960) and covered the journey of almost 6,000 miles in eight days.

THE CAPE TO CAIRO ROUTE

In 1880 Cecil Rhodes (1853–1902), a British colonial entrepreneur with extensive interests in southern Africa, conceived the dream of building a railway on British-ruled territory all the way from Cairo in Egypt to Cape Town in South Africa. In the event, the project ran into huge financial difficulties and Rhodes died before the line reached Victoria Falls. In 1904–5, a 198-metre long steel bridge, prefabricated in Darlington in northeast England, was built across the Zambezi River near the Falls. By 1906 the line had reached Broken Hill in Southern Rhodesia, today's Zimbabwe. It never got any further; the authorities in Egypt and the Sudan began to doubt the viability of the project and withdrew their funding.

Busy metropolis
Berlin grew rapidly at the end of the 19th century. Alexanderplatz station in the heart of the city (above left) was opened in 1882. Steam trains were replaced on this line by modern electric locomotives in 1928.

Marshalling yard
Electric locomotives and carriages beneath a forest of gantries and over-head lines at a busy marshalling yard outside Metz in eastern France.

supplies would be at a distinct advantage. Prussia's lead over France in developing such a network was a major factor in the crushing French defeat in the Franco-Prussian War of 1870–1. Germany's Schlieffen Plan for the invasion of France in the First World War was also based on mass troop mobilisation by rail. In the American Civil War, the North's extensive and well-run railway system allowed it to move men and supplies to the front far more efficiently than the Southern states. After the war, the mileage of track trebled in the space of just 30 years (from 1860 to 1890), and the railroad became a prime mover in the expansion and unification of the United States.

demand for capital and the prospect of quick profit were so great that ambitious, at times unscrupulous, bankers and venture capitalists queued up to lend money to railway companies. In 1857 in the USA, which by then had begun to make inroads into British dominance in the railway business, more than 1.1 billion dollars was invested in the railroads, more money than had ever been pumped into any other sector. Competition was fierce between German, French and British companies for the lucrative markets of South America and the Far East. For the first time, millions of small investors were tempted into buying shares in the railway boom.

Inevitably, in a Europe characterised by growing nationalism and tension, the railways became a key element in military strategy. Any nation with a good rail network that could quickly transport troops, arms and

Birth of a global sport

Soccer as we now know it came into being in 1863, when it broke away from rugby football and formed its own association. Since then it has gone from strength to strength, attracting ever more fans and becoming the world's most popular sport.

Ancient sport
A mosaic made in Sicily in the 3rd-4th century AD (right) shows a woman in sports attire throwing a ball. The coloured drawing (top right) is of an 18th-century Venetian nobleman playing football.

The birthplace of modern football was a noisy, smoky London pub, the Freemasons' Tavern, where representatives of 11 of the city's clubs plus Charterhouse school met on the evening of 26 October, 1863. Their aim was to establish a fundamental set of rules to govern the game. Five further meetings took place before the governing body of the newly formed Football Association finally settled on a code of 14 laws on 8 December, 1863. Among other things, these laws banned tripping, shin-kicking and handling the ball by outfield players, and their adoption marked the final split with devotees of Rugby football.

Ancient ball games

The meetings marked the official beginnings of football, but the game's true origins lie far back in history. Various ball games are known to have been played in ancient Greece, Asia and among pre-Columbian civilisations of Central America such as the Olmecs,

A MISLEADING NAME

The term 'football', first coined in England in 1486, does not derive from the fact that the game was played with the feet, but rather referred to the circumference of the ball itself: 1 foot = 30.48cm. Today, footballs are much bigger, with a circumference of 68–70cm and weighing 410–450 grams.

Maya and Aztecs. During the Middle Ages, ball games proliferated and became popular in Europe. In Britain, games of 'Shrovetide football' were held every Lent. These involved large unruly gangs of men and boys from neighbouring villages, each attempting to carry the ball into their opponents' territory. Games could last for many hours, even days, and violence was commonplace.

FROM BLADDERS TO MICROCHIPS

The oldest balls so far discovered have come from ancient Egyptian tombs. Ball games were widespread among ancient civilisations, using balls made of a variety of materials, including wood, leather, papyrus, bags of bran covered with skin, and even rubber (used by the Maya in a ritual ball game). From the Middle Ages to the 18th century, the most common type was a pig or ox bladder covered with hide; the bladder was inflated through a hole and tied like a balloon, then the covering hide was sewn shut with a lace. In around 1860, the Scottish firm of Charles Macintosh and Co replaced the animal bladder with one of vulcanised rubber. The use of panels of leather stitched together to form the outer casing persisted until the 1960s, when plastic-coated leather balls first appeared. These were followed in the 1980s by balls made entirely from synthetic materials. The latest innovation is a ball fitted with a microchip, which sends a radio signal to the referee's watch when it crosses the goal-line.

Revival in England

Between 1324 and 1667, no fewer than 30 royal and local edicts were passed outlawing unruly games of football. But at the beginning of the 19th century the country's prestigious public schools began to encourage the playing of football, not just for the healthy physical exercise it offered but also for the team spirit and sense of loyalty that it fostered. Before long, the precursor of modern football became an obligatory part of the school timetable. Attempts were made to organise matches, but the rules differed from school to school. Some practised passing and dribbling, while others favoured rucks and the use of hands. It was at one such institution, Rugby school, that a celebrated incident occurred in 1823, which many regard as the origin of rugby union. During a football match, a pupil named William Webb Ellis caught the ball, which was allowed, then ran with it, which was not, towards the opposing goal-line. The new game took the name of the school.

A growing rift

Many schools and clubs adopted the game of rugby football and authorised running while handling the ball. Yet others spurned the change. In 1848 representatives from Eton,

Football in art
After the rules of the various forms of football were formalised, artists began to take an interest in these popular sports. A Football Match (above) is a painting of 1894 after an engraving by W H Overend. The sculpture (left) was created by the American artist John Rogers in 1891 and is simply entitled Football.

Harrow, Rugby, Shrewsbury and Winchester met at Trinity College, Cambridge, to try to work out a set of standardised rules governing both football codes. The resulting Cambridge Rules laid down the dimensions of the pitch and the size of the goal and established the free kick. But the perennial debate about the use of hands and tripping was not resolved, nor could

Gridiron game
A photograph of the first encounter between the American football teams of Harvard and Yale, at Hamilton Park in Cambridge, Massachusetts, on 13 November, 1875.

Heavyweight footwear
Leather football boots dating from 1910. Early boots like these covered the ankles for protection. The first lightweight, low-profile soccer boots, manufactured by the German sports firm Adidas, came on the market in 1949. They had rubber soles and moulded studs.

they agree on the number of players per side. It was only at the Freemasons' Tavern meeting in 1863 that a decisive majority of clubs came down in favour of outlawing tripping, hacking and running while holding the ball.

The new rules were not to everyone's taste. Led by Francis Maude Campbell, a member of Blackheath Rugby Club, some clubs rejected the regulations and founded the Rugby Union. Adherents of the non-handling game founded the Football Association.

The irresistible rise of football

So began the inexorable rise of association football, or soccer. The first international fixture with the now standard 11 players on each side was played between England and Scotland in November 1870. England's premier domestic competition, the FA Cup, began the following year and within just a few years, cup ties were attracting more than

10,000 spectators. The thorny question of professionalism reared its head early on. At great expense, William Sudell, the chairman of Preston North End, signed up many of the top players of the day to create a 'dream team'. But during the FA Cup competition of 1884, another club challenged Sudell on the question of professionalism, who admitted that he was paying wages to his players and also revealed that he was not the only one doing so.

The administrators of the game were forced to confront the issue. In 1885, by a majority of 35 for to just 5 against, the FA voted to allow professionalism under certain conditions. Salaried players had to have been born, or have lived for at least 10 years, in the town whose club they played for. Thereafter, football really took off in England and the country dominated international contests until 1953, when a Hungarian team thrashed England by 6 goals to 3 on the hallowed turf of Wembley in their first ever home defeat.

Soccer goes global

Around the turn of the 19th century, national football associations were founded in several countries, including France (1881), New Zealand (1891), Uruguay and Germany (both 1900). The international governing body of the game – the Fédération Internationale de Football Association, better known as FIFA – was founded in Paris on 21 May, 1904. By 1912 it had 21 national associations affiliated to it; by 2010, that number had grown to 208.

Although the rules of the game have evolved over the decades, they remain basically the same as those formulated in the 1860s. The number of people playing the game has mushroomed; it is estimated that some 250 million people – around 1 in 27 of the global population – play football on a regular basis. Meanwhile, media coverage and the financing of football has increased out of all proportion. The 2006 World Cup in Germany attracted a television audience of some 26 billion over the course of the tournament, while FIFA, the principal sponsors, netted a cool 700 billion euros from the event.

AMERICAN FOOTBALL

Football and rugby were introduced into the United States in the early 1860s, but it was 1876 before universities there settled on a common set of laws. In the Massasoit Convention of that year, the rules governing Rugby Union were adopted wholesale except for a few minor differences in the scoring system. Then, in the 1880s, a sports coach at Yale University named Walter Camp radically altered the rules. He reduced the number of players from 15 to 11 per side, made the pitch smaller, introduced the 'line of scrimmage' and formulated the rule that a team failing to make an advance of 5 yards (4.5m) after three attempts must cede the ball to the opposition. This marked the birth of American Football. It soon became the most popular sport in the United States, but only made its debut in Europe in the 1980s. The International American Football Association was founded in 1998.

Skipper versus skipper
The French and Greek captains, Zinedine Zidane (right) and Theodoros Zagorakis, clash in the European Cup quarter finals in Portugal in 2004. France lost 1–0 and the Greeks went on to win the tournament, beating the host nation by the same score.

Heat treatment

In the early 1860s, the scientist Louis Pasteur was asked by Napoleon III of France to investigate why the country's wines were so prone to disease and did not travel well. This initiative ultimately led to the introduction of a process that is now universal in the food processing industry – pasteurisation.

Scientific tool
A replica of the glass carboy and swan-neck duct used by Pasteur in his experiments to investigate the role played by germs in causing disease.

Pasteur in his lab
An engraving shows the pioneer bacteriologist at work in his laboratory. After teaching at the universities of Strasbourg and Lille, Pasteur was appointed professor of chemistry at the Sorbonne in Paris in 1867. In recognition of the success of his anti-anthrax vaccine, The Times hailed him as 'one of the scientific glories of France'.

During the second half of the 19th century, following the signing of a trade accord between Britain and France, wine-growing developed into an important export earner for France. Sadly, French wines turned out to travel very badly; by the time they arrived at their destination, many had gone off and turned to vinegar in the bottle. Alarmed by the threat to the country's economy, Napoleon III asked Louis Pasteur to investigate the problem of diseases affecting wine.

The 41-year-old chemist and biologist had recently been elected to the French Academy of Sciences, having made a name for himself through his work on fermentation. By demonstrating the key role played by microorganisms (yeasts) in biochemical reactions, Pasteur hammered the first nail into the coffin of the theory of 'spontaneous generation'. For a long time, many scientists had thought that lower forms of life, such as insects, were not born via reproduction by parents, but instead arose 'out of nowhere' from inanimate matter. This theory had included among its adherents such notable figures as Descartes, Newton and Buffon. By proving that sterilised products could only ferment if yeasts were added to them, Pasteur helped to scotch this outmoded idea.

Careful research

Pasteur was delighted to accept the Emperor's commission. As a child, he had often watched winegrowers at work in his native Jura region in eastern France. He made regular return visits there, staying near Arbois, which was renowned for its sherry-like 'yellow wine'. In September 1863 Pasteur set up home in the Jura and began work. His first two months were spent doing experiments, interviewing winegrowers, visiting cellars, and taking notes and samples. He pinpointed four microbes at the root of different diseases affecting the

CONCLUSIVE PROOF

In his work on diseases of humans and animals Pasteur created an anti-anthrax vaccine. In May 1882 he used this to prove his 'germ theory' of disease transmission in a public test involving sheep. Two groups of 25 sheep were given the anthrax virus, but only one group were given the vaccine. The 25 uninoculated sheep soon died, whereas the inoculated group was 'gambolling about and showing every sign of perfect health'.

vinestock. In the wine trade, these are still known by the names that Pasteur gave them: *amertume* (intense bitterness, resulting from bacteria attacking the wine's natural glycerine); *graisse* (excessive viscosity); *tourne* (bacteria attack the wine's tartaric acid, making it less fruity and 'turning' it reddish-brown); and *acescence* (volatile acidity). These micro-organisms contaminate wine at different stages of its processing and ageing. Developing in particular conditions, they competed with the wine's natural fermentation.

Pasteur to the rescue

To combat these diseases, Pasteur first tried using antiseptics, but without success. His second approach was more effective: by briefly heating the wine to between 60°C and 100°C, he found that it kept better and retained its flavour. The discovery made French wine a viable export at last. Its inventor patented the process as 'pasteurisation' on 11 April, 1865. Yet because it also arrested the natural ageing process of wine, over the following decades vintners abandoned pasteurisation in favour of chemical treatments, such as sulphur dioxide, which allowed wine to continue to age.

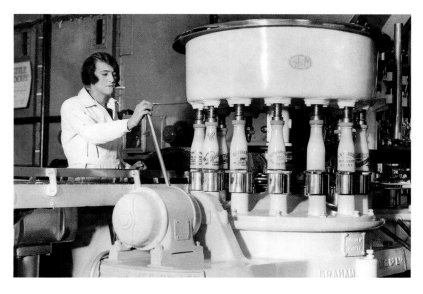

Model dairy
A milk-bottling machine in a clean, modern dairy plant of 1931.

Where pasteurisation did take permanent root was in the processing of other foodstuffs, such as beer, milk and fruit juice, where ageing was not an issue but going 'off' was. It gave these products the longest possible shelf life without impairing their flavour, and played a key role in the growth of the food-processing industry. Except in cold weather, milk could not normally be kept for more than 24 hours: pasteurisation revolutionised dairy farming.

Farm fresh

Largely as a result of pasteurisation, diseases such as bovine TB that could prove fatal to humans were eradicated from dairy produce and milk consumption spread far beyond country districts. A century after the invention of tinned food, the pasteurisation process introduced definitive standards of hygiene in the storage of foodstuffs, preventing them from being contaminated by bacteria.

Many other scientific and technological developments have contributed to the rise of the food industry since, including ionisation, sterilisation (heating beyond 100°C to kill virtually all germs) and chilled distribution networks. For extra long life, milk is sterilised by the UHT (ultra-high temperature) process, which heats it to between 135°C and 155°C for a few seconds. Refined versions of the original pasteurisation process are still used to conserve milk, ready meals, fruit and vegetables. After pasteurisation, some foodstuffs have a shelf life of between 6 and 12 months.

Milk for health
A schoolgirl from the 1920s tucks in to her lunch – a sandwich, banana and a bottle of pasteurised milk. Many governments adopted the distribution of free milk in schools to help children develop strong teeth and bones.

A man of many parts

Trained in both chemistry and biology, Pasteur not only invented a process that revolutionised industry and agriculture, but also pioneered vaccines against killer diseases such as rabies. At the root of his success lay a rigorous investigative method and a lively, inquiring mind.

Source of wealth
A print of 1870, now in the Pasteur Museum in Paris, shows a silkworm on a mulberry branch.

Louis Pasteur once famously claimed to 'occasionally cure, often alleviate, but always listen' – qualities we immediately associate with a doctor. Yet this leading therapist, whose work on infectious diseases and vaccines helped to save the lives of millions, never qualified as a physician. He was born in the town of Dole in the Jura region of France on 27 December, 1822, the son of a tanner. After studying locally, he was drawn to physics and chemistry and gained a doctorate from the elite École Normale Supérieure, which had been founded in Paris shortly after the Revolution. As a young lecturer in Dijon in 1848, he was the first to notice that organic molecules were asymmetrical; this helped to establish the phenomenon of optical activity, an important principle in organic chemistry. In 1854 he was appointed Dean of the Faculty of Sciences at the University of Lille. His work there on crystallography helped to generate a new branch of science – stereochemistry – and ultimately took him into a quite different field, namely fermentation. Pasteur discovered that fermentation was caused by the growth of living organisms, and that each type was the result of a specific microorganism. The science of microbiology was in its infancy, and Pasteur found himself increasingly drawn to this new discipline. As the 1860s proceeded, the investigative methods he developed from work in this field brought enormous benefits for industry and agriculture.

Aside from being a gifted theoretician, Pasteur was also very much a hands-on research scientist, and was keen to put his expertise at the service of professionals. He investigated the problems encountered by winegrowers and instructed them in how to achieve a consistent quality in their product. But his greatest contribution to viticulture was his invention of pasteurisation, a rapid heating process that killed off harmful bacteria.

In 1865 Pasteur was asked to tackle a mysterious epidemic, known as pebrine, that was devastating silkworm cultivation in the south of France. He discovered that it was caused by a hereditary and contagious microbe, the protozoan *Nosema bombycis*. His solution was to recommend the isolation and destruction of infected silkworms, and the selection only of eggs from healthy individuals for breeding.

Warfare on germs

By 1877 the 55-year-old Pasteur was suffering from serious health problems, but he threw himself eagerly into research on germs. He identified several bacteria, including staphylococcus (the cause of boils and bone infections) and streptococcus (responsible for puerperal fever, often following childbirth). He devised a number of vaccines, which he administered by inoculating the patient with a less virulent form of the bacterium in question; these included vaccines against cholera in chickens and rabies. At the same time, he made strenuous efforts to educate surgeons about the principles of asepsis and sterilisation to kill germs. Despite his international renown, Pasteur's ideas often met with opposition from his scientific colleagues at home.

Destined for greatness
A quiet determination shines out from this photograph of the young Louis Pasteur, taken in 1852 before he began his ground-breaking work on fermentation.

The father of immunology

Pasteur constantly struggled to get his ideas accepted by the French Academy of Medicine. At one meeting, he mocked one of his critics, the 80-year-old surgeon Jules Guérin, who responded by challenging him to a duel. Luckily, that particular fight never came to pass, but right up to his death, this brilliant and energetic scientist had to fight to defend his theories. His guiding principles of critical detachment and rigorous experimentation never wavered, and posterity has proved most of his theories right. His discoveries represented a giant leap forward in the fight against infectious diseases, while his work on vaccines made Pasteur the most celebrated founding father of the science of immunology.

Worldwide web
There is now a worldwide network of Pasteur Institutes, comprising 25 separate research institutions on five continents. They employ around 8,500 people, such as the biologist involved in experimentation below, most of whom are recruited locally.

COMBATING DISEASE

Founded in 1888, the Pasteur Institute is primarily dedicated to the fight against contagious diseases. An autonomous organisation, it specialises in microbiology, immunology and molecular biology, and boasts many Nobel laureates among its past and present staff.

PASTEUR'S GUINEA-PIG

On 6 July, 1885, a nine-year-old boy from Alsace, Joseph Meister, and his mother appeared at Louis Pasteur's laboratory in Paris. Two days before, Joseph had been bitten by a rabid dog. Realising that he had to act fast to save the boy's life, Pasteur decided to administer his brand-new anti-rabies vaccine, the first time he had given it to a human. Prior to this, low-dose preparations of the virus – made from the bone marrow of rabid rabbits – had only been tried on dogs. Over ten days, Joseph received daily injections of increasingly strong preparations of the vaccine in his chest (below). He recovered fully and went on to lead a healthy life.

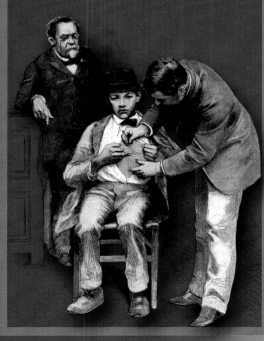

Trains under the city

The London Underground came about through the dogged determination of one man. Before long it was a model for urban transport systems worldwide. Running either underground or on elevated tracks, metropolitan railways offered a fast new way of getting about in cities.

Growing network
A map of London's underground railways (right), drawn up in the late 19th century, shows the geograpical routes of the lines existing at the time. The celebrated schematic map drawn by Harry Beck, on which the modern Tube map is based, was not introduced until 1931.

Cut and cover
Construction of the Metropolitan Railway near King's Cross in 1861 (above). For much of its length, the line followed the Marylebone–Euston Road and was built by the 'cut and cover' method. A large trench was dug in the road, and wooden casements erected over it as temporary supports for a brick tunnel. When the tunnel was complete, the trench was backfilled to cover it.

On 10 January, 1863, three years of Herculean effort – and massive disruption – finally came to fruition in London with the grand opening of the new underground railway link from Paddington Station to Farringdon Street. Sadly, the man who had been the inspiration behind the project, the City solicitor and campaigner Charles Pearson, did not live to see it, having died the previous September. The Metropolitan Railway was the first underground railway line in the world, and it was an instant success. Before long, some 26,000 people were taking its trains daily.

A long gestation

The idea of trains running beneath cities had been put forward as early as the 1830s, but at that time technology was not sufficiently advanced to bring the plan to fruition. In 1845 Pearson published a pamphlet calling for the construction of a line running from the centre of London through the valley of the Fleet River to Farringdon. Pearson, a solicitor and councillor on the City of London Corporation, was acutely aware of the growing congestion choking London's business district. His suggestions failed to excite immediate interest but did represent the starting point for his lengthy campaign to establish a railway network within the capital. There was certainly a need for one: by mid-century, London had 2.5 million inhabitants, the most populous city in the world, and was regularly experiencing gridlock on an epic scale. Massive traffic jams were caused by the horse-drawn omnibuses and hackney cabs that brought thousands of workers from the mainline railway terminuses into the City every day.

TWO ENGINEERS FOR THE TUBE

John Fowler and Marc Isambard Brunel (father of Isambard Kingdom) pioneered underground engineering works in London, but they went about it in very different ways. To build the Metropolitan Line, Fowler used the 'cut and cover' method. He went on to build the Forth Railway Bridge in Scotland, the world's first all-steel cantilever bridge. Brunel, by contrast, patented a tunnelling shield to tunnel directly through the subsoil. Using this device, in 1825 he began digging a tunnel between Rotherhithe and Wapping, 23m beneath the Thames. Designed for horse-drawn carriages, the tunnel opened – just to pedestrians – in 1843 and is thought to be the first tunnel under a major river anywhere in the world. It was converted to take trains from 1869 and is still part of London's rail network today.

THE FORGOTTEN TUNNEL

While the city of New York was busy constructing its elevated railway, Alfred Ely Beach, inventor and editor of *Scientific American*, devised a different plan. Inspired by London's Metropolitan Railway, and also by the pneumatic-tube mail delivery system built there in 1866, he conceived an 'atmospheric railway': a line on which the trains ran in hermetically sealed tunnels, drawn along by compressed air. He secured a loan to build a pneumatic postal tube and instead used it to construct a 100m section of track and a show station under Broadway, which he opened for display on 26 February, 1870. But Beach failed to get permission to extend his tunnel; it was abandoned in 1873 and forgotten. In 1912, when workers were excavating the New York Subway, they came across Beach's tunnel and station, complete with train, still intact. It was demolished to build City Hall Station.

In 1852 Pearson and others founded the City Terminus Company, which was set up specifically to build the line to Farringdon, but Parliament refused to provide funds for the project. Then the following year a rival enterprise – the Bayswater, Paddington and Holborn Bridge Railway Company – put forward a plan for a North Metropolitan Railway and immediately got a green light from government. The two companies merged in 1854 and a Royal Commission was appointed to study the various schemes.

Pearson's proposal was to link all seven mainline terminus stations then surrounding the City, namely London Bridge, Waterloo, Paddington, Euston, King's Cross, Shoreditch and Fenchurch Street (the only station actually within the City). Acting on the Commission's report, Parliament approved the building of a line from Paddington to Farringdon Street via King's Cross and Islington, a distance of 4 miles. The Metropolitan Railway thus came into being; its name, abbreviated to 'metro', came to be used for underground railways the world over. By February 1860, the company had assembled all the funding necessary for work to commence.

Hot and smoky

Jubilant scenes greeted the first trial run of the Metropolitan Railway in 1862. Initially passengers travelled in open trucks.

Subterranean London

A cross-section, made in 1865, of the underground utilities beneath Hampstead Road shows, from top to bottom, the water main, a pneumatic tube system for carrying mail, the Northern Line and a projected link (never built) between Hampstead Road and Charing Cross station.

Underground overground
Elevated trains running in New York in the 1920s (below). Despite being called the 'subway', around 40 per cent of New York's metropolitan commuter railway network still runs on overhead tracks. Some 5 million people use the network each day. The illustration (inset, right) shows a crowd of New Yorkers jostling to get on the subway after work on a rainy evening in 1890.

RIDING THE 'EL'

The Americans preferred to avoid the disruption of digging subway tunnels under their new cities, opting instead for a system of tracks elevated on cast-iron, steel or, later, concrete gantries. The elevated railway track – known as the 'El' for short – became a quintessential symbol of New York and Chicago. The first line in New York, the West Side and Yonkers Patent Railway, was opened in 1868. Running the length of Ninth Avenue, it formed the first section of the overhead network. After New York expanded in 1898 to take in the neighbouring towns of Brooklyn, Queens and Staten Island, the city authorities decided to invest in a subway network, the first part of which was opened on 27 October, 1904, in Manhattan. In this exclusive downtown area, where land prices are astronomically high, all lines have long since gone underground.

Herculean effort

Constructing a railway line in a built-up city posed a massive challenge. There were two possible ways to go about it: either dig tunnels beneath the streets or construct overhead tracks above them. London chose the former and John Fowler, the Metropolitan Railway's chief engineer, set about digging tunnels using the only viable technique then available: the

cut-and-cover method. Entire slum districts were razed to accommodate the new line. Where houses survived, residents had to endure the inconvenience of the road being completely dug up to allow the construction of the tunnel, before it could be filled in and the road replaced. Predictably, the excavations ran into difficulties, such as one occasion when the Fleet River – a tributary of the Thames long used as a sewer – burst into the workings.

A major problem that Fowler had to address was how to prevent the steam and smoke emissions from the engines asphyxiating the passengers in tunnels. His solution was to design an engine that would run without an open fire to heat the boiler – 'Fowler's Ghost' would use heat stored in firebricks to generate steam. A prototype was built by Robert Stephenson's company in Newcastle, but it was a complete failure as the firebricks were too

Travelling in style
Commuters on the New York subway in 1901. Today there are officially 468 stations on the system – even more if one counts stations that are closed and complexes that comprise several stations. This makes it the world's largest underground network in terms of stations served.

inefficient at heat storage. The Metropolitan was forced to revert to more conventional locomotives, built by Beyer, Peacock and Company of Manchester, but which directed their exhaust steam back into the water tank, where much of it was condensed. The tunnels still needed to be ventilated for the smoke and so Fowler had a series of enormous ventilation shafts built to clear the smoke from the tunnels and allow fresh air to enter. To preserve the uniform appearance of certain streets, several of these vents were concealed behind false façades that looked like normal house fronts.

Developing a network

Despite being a great success, the Metropolitan only went a small way towards relieving London's congestion. It represented merely the first step on the way to creating an 'Inner Circle' linking all the mainline railway termini. Between 1864 and 1868, the Metropolitan extended its line to South Kensington. At the same time, the company constructed overland tracks to the southwestern suburbs, such as the line to Richmond in 1877. These lines proved extremely profitable, and for a while deflected effort away from expansion of the inner-city network. But the Metropolitan was not the only company involved: the Metropolitan District Railway was founded in 1864 with the aim of linking Westminster to South Kensington via Victoria. Work got underway on the project on 24 December, 1868. The District, like its rival, funded its operations by building lines out into the suburbs.

The Circle Line was finally completed on 6 October, 1884. It was to become the core of a much larger network, under the direction

---

THE PARIS MÉTRO

The first line on the Paris Métro was opened on 19 July, 1900. It was built for the World's Fair, which was held in the city that year, and its stations were given beautifully ornate ironwork and glass entrances designed in the Art Nouveau style by Hector Guimard. By the 1920s, a network of lines criss-crossed the entire city. As Paris expanded after the Second World War, the system became overloaded, leading to the construction in the 1960s of a second network, the RER, which was designed to serve outlying suburbs. Inspired by the London Underground, this dual system (comprising inner and outer zones) serves many of the towns surrounding the capital.

Catching up *Intensive work was carried out in the early 1900s to give Paris an extensive underground network like that in London. These workmen (below) are digging a tunnel under the River Seine, downstream of the Pont de la Concorde in 1911.*

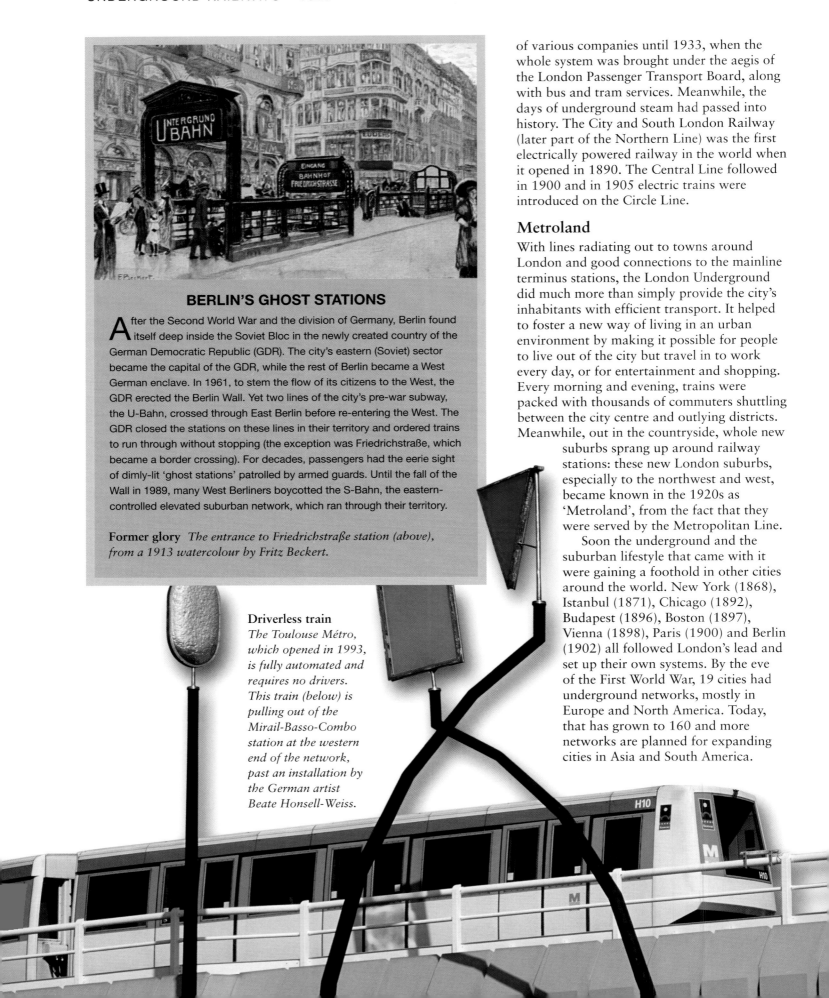

BERLIN'S GHOST STATIONS

After the Second World War and the division of Germany, Berlin found itself deep inside the Soviet Bloc in the newly created country of the German Democratic Republic (GDR). The city's eastern (Soviet) sector became the capital of the GDR, while the rest of Berlin became a West German enclave. In 1961, to stem the flow of its citizens to the West, the GDR erected the Berlin Wall. Yet two lines of the city's pre-war subway, the U-Bahn, crossed through East Berlin before re-entering the West. The GDR closed the stations on these lines in their territory and ordered trains to run through without stopping (the exception was Friedrichstraße, which became a border crossing). For decades, passengers had the eerie sight of dimly-lit 'ghost stations' patrolled by armed guards. Until the fall of the Wall in 1989, many West Berliners boycotted the S-Bahn, the eastern-controlled elevated suburban network, which ran through their territory.

Former glory *The entrance to Friedrichstraße station (above), from a 1913 watercolour by Fritz Beckert.*

Driverless train
The Toulouse Métro, which opened in 1993, is fully automated and requires no drivers. This train (below) is pulling out of the Mirail-Basso-Combo station at the western end of the network, past an installation by the German artist Beate Honsell-Weiss.

of various companies until 1933, when the whole system was brought under the aegis of the London Passenger Transport Board, along with bus and tram services. Meanwhile, the days of underground steam had passed into history. The City and South London Railway (later part of the Northern Line) was the first electrically powered railway in the world when it opened in 1890. The Central Line followed in 1900 and in 1905 electric trains were introduced on the Circle Line.

Metroland

With lines radiating out to towns around London and good connections to the mainline terminus stations, the London Underground did much more than simply provide the city's inhabitants with efficient transport. It helped to foster a new way of living in an urban environment by making it possible for people to live out of the city but travel in to work every day, or for entertainment and shopping. Every morning and evening, trains were packed with thousands of commuters shuttling between the city centre and outlying districts. Meanwhile, out in the countryside, whole new suburbs sprang up around railway stations: these new London suburbs, especially to the northwest and west, became known in the 1920s as 'Metroland', from the fact that they were served by the Metropolitan Line.

Soon the underground and the suburban lifestyle that came with it were gaining a foothold in other cities around the world. New York (1868), Istanbul (1871), Chicago (1892), Budapest (1896), Boston (1897), Vienna (1898), Paris (1900) and Berlin (1902) all followed London's lead and set up their own systems. By the eve of the First World War, 19 cities had underground networks, mostly in Europe and North America. Today, that has grown to 160 and more networks are planned for expanding cities in Asia and South America.

Radio and electromagnetic waves 1864

In a celebrated extract from his 1864 work *A dynamical theory of the electromagnetic field*, Scottish physicist James Clerk Maxwell (1831–79) stated: 'Light and magnetism are affections of the same substance … light is an electromagnetic disturbance propagated through the field according to electromagnetic laws.' It was here that Maxwell revealed, for the first time, that electricity and magnetism were two different manifestations of the same phenomenon, namely the electromagnetic field. It confirmed the fact that light itself emanated from this field. Maxwell meant 'light' in its wider sense, encompassing both visible light and invisible light waves (such as infra red).

An unexpected discovery

Maxwell's findings were a spin-off from his research into magnetism and electricity. These cutting-edge areas of enquiry derived from the Danish physicist Hans Christian Oersted's 1819 discovery that an electric current creates magnetism and Michael Faraday's insight in 1831 that changes in a magnetic field can induce electricity. In trying to grasp the interrelation, Maxwell hit upon a surprising fact: that self-propagating electromagnetic waves travel through space at a constant speed equal to that of light.

Maxwell died in 1879 without realising the far-reaching implications of his work. Not only would all modern forms of telecommunication, such as radio and TV, rely on electromagnetic waves, but they also became a vital tool in medicine (radiotherapy, X-rays), in probing the Solar System (radioastronomy) and studying matter in microcosmic detail (lasers).

In the ether
The electromagnetic waves emitted by radio antennae are invisible, but are traditionally represented graphically, as here, by concentric circles.

TOWARDS THE WIRELESS

In 1887, the German physicist Heinrich Rudolf Hertz confirmed Maxwell's theories beyond all doubt. Hertz produced electromagnetic waves from a high-voltage spark discharge, via a pair of paddle-like plates, a dipole antenna. Nearby, he placed a receiving antenna, in the form of two brass balls set close together. Each time the large primary spark jumped across the dipole antenna, a tiny spark flickered between the balls of the receiving antenna. This was wireless communication in action, which in time would lead to the development of the radio.

Scanning the skies *The VLA (Very Large Array) in New Mexico is a radio astronomy observatory comprising 27 separate parabolic reflectors, each 25m in diameter, arranged in a huge 'Y' formation. The purpose of the VLA is to investigate astronomical phenomena such as radio galaxies, quasars, pulsars and supernovae.*

THE SUEZ CANAL
A new route to the East

The Suez Canal first opened to shipping in 1869. Running from Port Said on the Mediterranean coast to Suez on the Red Sea, it had an immediate and dramatic impact on world maritime trade.

Two views
A modern satellite photograph (above) shows the Mediterranean and Nile Delta at the top, Great Bitter Lake at the canal's mid-point and the Red Sea at its southern end. The sepia photograph (left) shows ships docked at Port Said in October 1875, en route to India with the Prince of Wales, the future Edward VII, on board. Soon after, Prime Minister Disraeli acquired almost half of the canal for Britain.

By the mid-19th century, transportation by sea of raw materials and manufactured goods was booming as never before. Within three decades of the first transatlantic crossing by a steamship in 1838, the advent of all-metal hulls and screw propulsion had transformed the speed and reliability of such vessels. Steamers completed the passage from New York to London on average 10 days quicker than sailing ships. And while tea clippers, the fastest sailing ships afloat, could make the journey from the Far East to England in three months, steam vessels were soon covering the same distance in two. Between 1820 and 1850, the growth in the tonnage of ships brought down the cost of transporting goods by sea by 75 per cent. This made it far more economical to carry goods by ship between Europe and Asia rather than overland. Opening up new sea routes became a priority for the major powers as they pursued commercial expansion and the development of overseas empires.

European rivalry
Ever since Napoleon's expedition to Egypt in 1798, influential people in France had harboured a dream of cutting a canal across the isthmus of Suez to create a navigable link between the Mediterranean and the Red Sea. If this could be achieved, then instead of having to sail right round Africa to reach India and the Far East, ships from the Mediterranean could slip through the canal, down the Red Sea and out into the Indian Ocean.

Lightening the load
Digging the Suez Canal was a vast undertaking. Increasingly, earth-moving machines, as shown in this engraving of 1870 (above), took on work formerly done by armies of men.

At the instigation of the diplomat Count Ferdinand de Lesseps (1805–94), work on the canal began in 1859. The chosen route ran for a distance of 102 miles through Lake Timsah and the Bitter Lakes and did not require locks. First, in order to channel water from the Nile into the new canal, a feeder canal was dug by an army of some 20,000 pickaxe-wielding *fellahin* (Egyptian peasants or farm workers), who had been seconded as labourers by Said Pasha, the Khedive of Egypt.

The British saw the canal as a threat to their monopoly of the seaborne trade routes to India and feared the spread of French influence in the region, so they pressurised the Ottoman Empire (Egypt's masters at the time) into halting construction work. France's Napoleon III responded by dispatching 15,000 European labourers to the site, along with an impressive array of heavy machinery, including dredgers, hoists, barges and special lighters that used compressed air to pump out the excavated silt. This new, well-equipped workforce completed the canal by 1869. When first opened to ships, the canal was 52 metres wide in total, with a 22-metre central channel dredged to a depth of 8 metres.

The canal was not the instant success its backers had hoped for. Before long financial difficulties forced Ismail Pasha, successor to Said, to sell all of Egypt's shares in the enterprise. Prime Minister Benjamin Disraeli, with financial backing from the Rothschilds, stepped in to buy them on behalf of the British government. The canal thus came under joint French and British administration, and work on improving the waterway began in 1876.

The Suez Canal today

In 1888 the canal was declared a neutral zone, with guaranteed right of passage for all ships; it was nationalised by Egypt in 1956. Since the construction of channels running out into the Mediterranean and Red Sea, the total length of the canal has grown to 120 miles; the average width has grown to 365 metres, the central 190 metres of which is fully navigable. For 42 miles of its length the canal has twin shipping lanes, allowing ships to pass one another without stopping. Work is underway to increase the depth from 20.13 to 23.38 metres to enable tankers up to 350,000 tonnes deadweight to use it. In 2008 a total of 21,415 ships used the canal, carrying 723 million tonnes of cargo and earning Egypt $3.3 billion in transit fees, five times more than in 1964. Both economically and geopolitically, the Suez Canal remains a vital global transport link.

New crossing
The Centennial Bridge over the Panama Canal (below) was built to ease the traffic load on the ageing nearby Bridge of the Americas. The new bridge, which carries the Panamerican Highway, was opened in 2004.

THE PANAMA CANAL

In 1880 Ferdinand de Lesseps began an even greater challenge: cutting a canal across the isthmus of Panama. From the outset the enterprise was dogged by financial scandal and disease. The workforce was devastated by malaria and yellow fever, and the project was abandoned in 1893. Work restarted under American control after Panama gained nominal independence in 1903. A team led by US army engineer George W Goethals overcame the considerable obstacles to complete the canal in 1914. It enables ships to avoid the treacherous passage around Cape Horn and cuts 15,000 miles off the sea voyage from New York to San Francisco. The canal is 50 miles long and has two series of locks – at Milaflores and Gatún. In 2008, with the passage of some 309 million tonnes of cargo, the canal was operating at almost maximum capacity. Work is now underway to enlarge the canal by 2014.

ANTISEPTICS – 1867

Hygienic hospitals

Inspired by the work of Louis Pasteur, the British surgeon Joseph Lister pioneered the use of antiseptics in surgery. This not only saved the lives of thousands of patients but also paved the way for the rigorous use of antiseptic sterilisation in operating theatres.

When Joseph Lister was just embarking on his career as a surgeon in Edinburgh in the 1850s, he witnessed at first hand the ravages of post-operative infections. The son of a Quaker family from Essex and a graduate of the faculty of medicine at London University, Lister had opted for a career in surgery after marrying the daughter of an eminent Scottish surgeon. The increasing use of anaesthetics from the 1840s onwards had made operating theatres calmer places, but undergoing an operation was still a very risky business. Following amputations, some patients developed a redness around the wound, rapidly followed by a severe fever and uncontrollable shivering. These were symptoms of a painful infection known as erysipelas, which often proved fatal. Others succumbed to gangrene, which made the wound smell appalling, or to tetanus. On average, 40 per cent of all patients failed to survive an amputation. James Simpson, a famous Scottish surgeon who pioneered the use of chloroform as an anaesthetic, wrote in 1867 that 'the man laid on the operating-table in one of our surgical hospitals is exposed to more chances of death than the English soldier on the field of Waterloo'. Even nonoperative patients with, say, a compound fracture or just a simple cut ran the risk of dying through blood poisoning. Faced with this dreadful rate of attrition, Lister set himself the task of locating the origin of post-operative infections and finding ways to combat them.

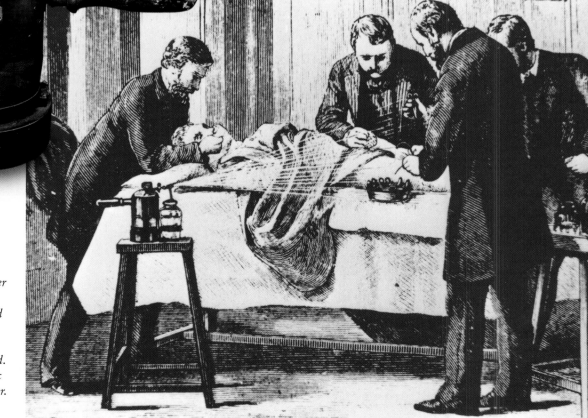

Safer surgery
A print of c1870 (right) shows a contemporary aseptic operating theatre. The diffuser on the stool in the foreground sprayed a fine mist of carbolic acid over the patient's wound. Above: the carbolic spray used by Lister.

80

Best practice
Scrubbing-up is the basis of asepsis in modern hospitals. In accordance with World Health Organisation guidelines, water–alcohol solutions have gradually replaced antiseptic carbolic soap for this procedure.

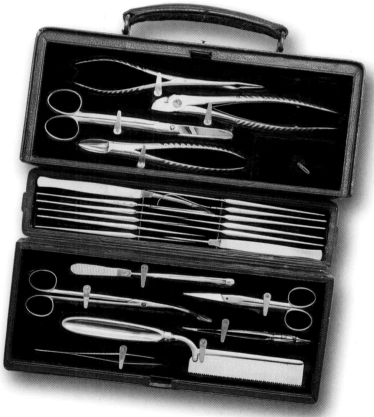

Stopping wounds festering

In 1860 Lister was appointed Professor of Surgery at the University of Glasgow. His studies led him to the germ theory of disease recently put forward by the French biologist and chemist Louis Pasteur. From his work on the storage properties of beer and wine, Pasteur had discovered that microorganisms, which multiplied under certain conditions, were at the root of all disease. The findings were a revelation to Lister. He became convinced that pus was not a natural by-product of scar tissue, as most doctors thought at the time, but rather the result of bacteria from the skin or the air getting into the wound and infecting it. Accordingly, Lister began swabbing patients'

Precision instruments
A surgical kit from the late 19th century (above). By this stage, stainless steel was being used, which withstood the steam sterilising process.

wounds with carbolic acid (phenol). Carbolic was already widely used to deodorise sewage; Lister had learned that effluent treated in this way and spread on a field at Carlisle had eradicated a parasite causing disease in cattle. In 1865 a man named James Cobb became Lister's first guinea pig. Rather than operate on an open wound on Cobb's thigh, Lister covered it with a compress soaked in phenol. Within three months, the wound had healed up without festering and the patient was fully recovered. Lister followed this up with other equally notable successes. In 1867 he published his initial clinical observations and his principles of antiseptics in a series of articles that appeared in the *Lancet* and the *British Medical Journal*.

Carbolic in the operating theatre

Lister also used carbolic to disinfect surgeons' coats, the drains in operating rooms and the catgut that was used to stitch open wounds. He sprayed a fine mist of it into the air during operations and required surgeons to wash their instruments and their hands in a carbolic solution before operating. He was clear about his aims: 'It is vital to prevent germs from entering the wound both during and after the operation … All instruments, linen and as a general principle everything that comes into contact with the wound during the operation, including the surgeon's hands and those of his assistants, must be made antiseptic'.

A MEETING OF MINDS

On 18 February, 1874, Lister wrote to Pasteur to thank him for having shown him, through his 'brilliant research, the truth about germs of putrefaction' and 'having set forth the sole principle that might successfully establish the antiseptic system'.

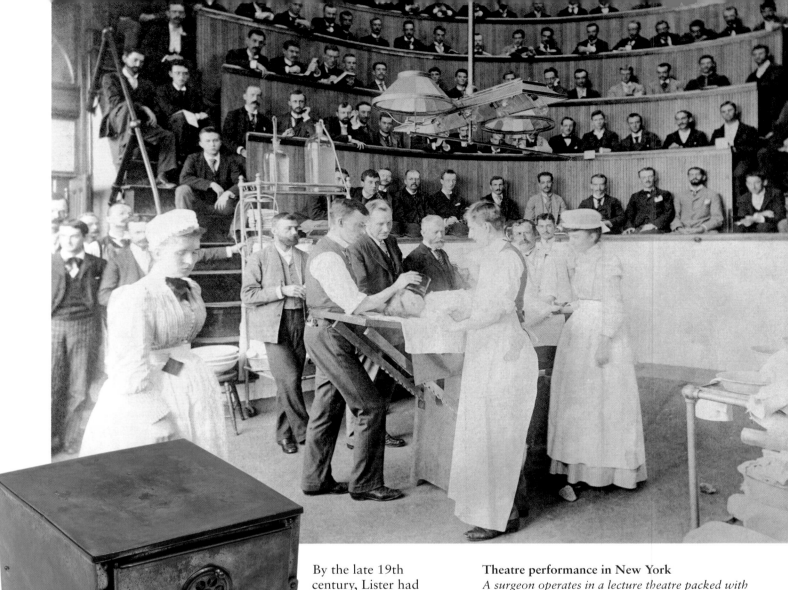

Theatre performance in New York
A surgeon operates in a lecture theatre packed with medical students in 1898. This unhygienic practice was long established and clung on tenaciously. Most surgeons thought of bacteria as a zoological curiosity that had nothing to do with their world.

Steam treatment
A copper autoclave from the late 19th century used for sterilising surgical instruments (above).

By the late 19th century, Lister had established all the basic principles of asepsis – the eradication of disease-causing germs – and antiseptics. The former consisted of stopping bacteria from getting into the patient, while the latter involved killing bacteria as an integral step in the treatment or prevention of infection. Lister's department saw the mortality rate of amputees drop from 40 per cent to 15 per cent. The incidence of suppurating wounds also fell dramatically.

Even so, Lister met with resistance from many of his colleagues. His methods overturned time-honoured procedures. Most surgeons still preferred to operate in frock coats, blithely dipping their sleeves and their unwashed bare hands into patients' wounds. Sterile conditions were alien to most operating theatres; open galleries were packed with students, and autopsies were also carried out in the same rooms. Hygiene was also lax in post-operative care, with the same sponge often being used to

swab the wounds of all the patients on a ward and only rinsed in water in between.

Another misunderstood pioneer

Lister was not the only one to upset the medical establishment. In around 1847, an Austro-Hungarian obstetrician by the name of Ignaz Semmelweis encountered similar resistance when he tried to introduce hand-washing as standard procedure. Yet the results he achieved were astonishing. In the maternity ward where he worked in Vienna, almost one in three women was dying of puerperal fever after giving birth. Mysteriously, this disease (whose cause was then unknown) was virtually absent from a similar ward in another hospital, staffed entirely by midwives. Semmelweis got to the root of the problem when he noticed that medical students in his department were coming straight from the autopsy room to the

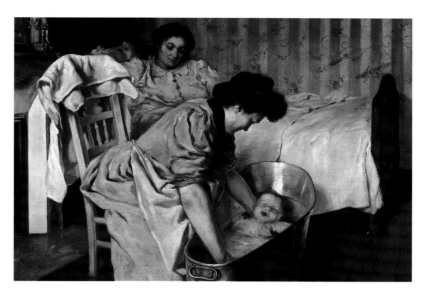

maternity ward, carrying germs picked up from cadavers. The midwives, on the other hand, had no contact with dissections. Semmelweis made his students wash their hands in a solution of calcium chloride, and puerperal fever disappeared almost overnight from his delivery room. For his pains, he found himself dismissed by his employers.

Twenty years later, Lister fared somewhat better in trying to get carbolic adopted as standard disinfection procedure. His methods were taken up in Germany and France. Antiseptics and anaesthetics transformed surgical practice beyond all recognition. Surgical interventions – now more geared to preserving healthy organs and tissue – became far less traumatic and invasive. Hospital-acquired infections plummeted and with them the number of deaths resulting from surgery.

The beginnings of sterilisation

Lister's work paved the way for hospital hygiene. Many improvements followed in the later 19th century. Because toxic disinfectants like phenol were effectively useless for certain operations, such as on the digestive tract, antiseptic media were introduced such as chlorinated products, potassium permanganate, and alcohol-based preparations. At the same time, asepsis became increasingly important. In place of the old miasma theory of germs, doctors began to realise the importance of sterilising everything that came into contact with the operating table. Surgeons donned special smocks, while scrubbing-up became standard procedure.

Safe delivery
This 1902 painting by the Spanish artist Leopoldo Garciá Ramón shows a midwife bathing a newborn baby. Before the advent of sterilisation and antiseptics, women giving birth at home were less prone to puerperal fever than those who went into hospital.

Sterile rubber gloves first appeared at this time. Water, dressings and instruments were all sterilised in steam autoclaves before operations. Proper purpose-built operating theatres were constructed, while hospital interiors were designed with an eye to ease of cleaning.

Although clinical hygiene improved steadily throughout the 20th century, the recent emergence of tenacious hospital-acquired infections such as MRSA demonstrates that the fight to maintain safe, aseptic conditions continues to be of the highest priority.

Ongoing fight
For all the advances in hygiene, hospital-acquired infections continue to give cause for concern; such diseases now affect between 5 per cent and 12 per cent of all in-patients in European hospitals.

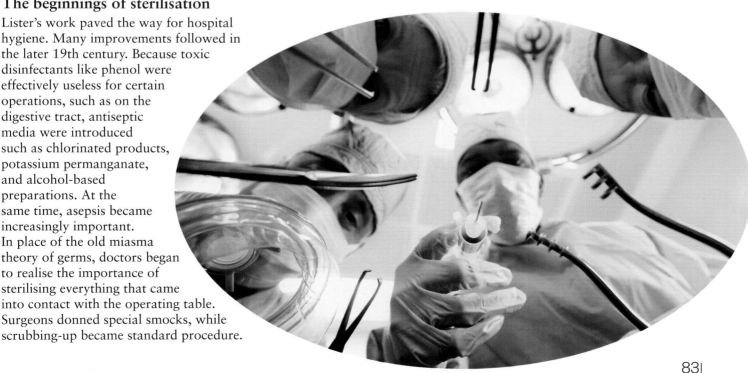

The Leclanché cell 1867

Key breakthrough
Leclanché's cell was a great improvement on the Voltaic pile. The main problem with the original version of 1866–7 (below) was that the liquid electrolyte was prone to leakage and spillage when transported.

Georges Leclanché was born in Paris in 1839. Due to his lawyer father's (and later his own) opposition to the French government, most of his early life was spent abroad in exile, and it was in Brussels in 1863 that he first became interested in electrochemical research. Returning to Paris in 1864, he secured a job as a chemist in the materials laboratory of a French railway company. There he set about designing an improved version of the primary electrochemical cell, now better known to most people as a battery.

Ideal for telegraphy

In 1867 Leclanché unveiled his new invention. In his battery, the cathode (the positive terminal) was comprised of a carbon rod sealed in a porous pot. The pot was packed with a solid depolariser made from a mixture of crushed manganese dioxide and conductive carbon powder. This arrangement solved the problem of polarisation that had dogged the Voltaic pile. The cathode and the zinc anode (the negative terminal) were immersed in a jar of ammonium chloride solution. This liquid acted as the electrolyte, carrying electric current through the porous pot to the cathode. Leclanché's battery proved to be powerful, reliable and safe. Best of all, it only discharged when it was in use.

It was not long before the Belgian telegraph service, then the Dutch, began using the Leclanché cell, which was ideal for delivering an electromotive force of around 1.5 volts and required little maintenance. The technology was soon adopted by manufacturers, finding

widespread use in early telephones, electric torches and bells. Later refinements included the Leclanché-Barbier cell (1878), the dry-cell battery (1887) developed by the Dane Frederik Hellsen and Carl Gassner's zinc–carbon battery of the same year, which used a paste of ammonium chloride and plaster of Paris for the electrolyte. It was Gassner's cell that became the model for the modern dry-cell battery, a key component in watches, mobile phones, video recorders, remote-control units and a host of other electronic appliances.

From wet to dry
Although the Leclanché cell was a wet-cell battery, the chemicals it used were cheap, safe and readily adaptable to dry-cell technology. Leclanché's invention has a strong claim to being the ancestor of the familiar battery used in so many modern appliances.

ROOM FOR IMPROVEMENT

The Voltaic pile, the very first battery that converted chemical energy into electricity, was unreliable and ran down quickly. The zinc of the anode became oxidised and corroded, while hydrogen bubbles formed on the cathode, impeding the passage of electrons and so increasing the battery's internal resistance. This phenomenon, known as 'polarisation', had the effect of gradually weakening the current flowing between the two electrodes. None of the immediate successors to the Voltaic pile was much better. In 1839 Welsh physicist William Robert Grove developed an electric cell in which a platinum cathode was immersed in concentrated nitric acid. Although this acted as a depolariser, preventing the formation of hydrogen, in operation it gave off highly toxic nitrogen dioxide fumes.

Barbed wire 1867

In the mid-19th century, as pioneers settled the American Midwest, they needed a way to corral their herds and to protect their field crops from straying animals. The problem was especially bad in the Mississippi region, where the absence of trees and rocks made it virtually impossible to enclose land effectively. One idea for replacing traditional wooden or sagebrush fences was to use iron wire; the drawback was that it went slack in extreme heat, while in cold weather it became brittle and could snap, allowing determined animals to get through.

In 1867 a US inventor patented a barbed attachment for single-strand wire, designed to repel animals. Then, seven years later, a farmer in Illinois named Joseph Glidden patented a double-strand wire with the barbs twisted firmly in place to make them unslippable. At the same time, he patented a machine to mass-produce it. Glidden's invention was adopted throughout the USA and then the rest of the world, replacing hedges and wooden fences. Various types have since been developed, most recently razor wire for use around high-security facilities like military bases.

Effective barrier *Barbed wire was first used to enclose the prairies of the American Midwest as farmland, but it also found a ready military application in the trench warfare of the First World War as a highly effective defence against infantry advances. The British developed the tank largely in order to overcome such defences.*

Margarine 1869

Butter was once a luxury beyond the reach of many people, especially the urban poor. It cost a lot and did not keep well. In 1869 Napoleon III of France offered a prize to anyone who could 'invent a satisfactory substitute for butter, suitable for use by the navy and the working classes'. The challenge was taken up by chemist Hippolyte Mège-Mouriès (1817–80), who had experience in the food-processing industry. His aim was to make a product that would not go rancid so quickly.

On 15 July, 1869, he lodged a patent for a butter substitute made from processed beef tallow blended with skimmed milk. He named his new product 'oleomargarine', subsequently shortened to margarine for its pearlescent colour (*margaron* is Greek for 'pearl oyster'). In 1872 Mège-Mouriès sold his process to the Dutch manufacturer Jurgens (later part of

Cheaper than butter *A 1921 French advert stresses the cost-effectiveness of margarine. A key ingredient of La Végétaline', first manufactured in 1896, was coconut oil, extracted from the kernel of the nut (copra).*

Unilever). It was soon available in Britain as 'butterine'. Later, after the development of the hydrogenation process by which liquid oils are converted into solid or semi-solid fats, butter substitutes could be made from palm and coconut oils. Other techniques involve emulsifying milk, water and vegetable oils. Despite its rather artificial taste, the affordability of margarine made it an instant bestseller.

The vacuum cleaner 1869

Mechanical solution
The Bissell carpet sweeper (left) was invented in 1876 by Melville Bissell. After his death in 1889, his wife Anna became the first woman to head a major company.

House-proud
An advertisement of 1906 for Booth's British Vacuum Cleaner Company (below), and one of Booth's mighty machines in operation at a smart London address (bottom right).

The first vacuum cleaner – an industrial suction apparatus for ridding houses of dust – was patented in 1869 by the Chicago inventor Ives W McGaffy. His 'Whirlwind' comprised an inverted fan driven by a crank to create suction, but the device was unwieldy, ineffectual and a commercial failure. Further development was halted when McGaffy's workshop was destroyed in the Great Fire that swept through Chicago in 1871.

Mother of invention

Five years later businesswoman Anna Bissell, who ran a china shop in Grand Rapids, Michigan, complained to her husband Melville about the incessant chore of sweeping up sawdust from packing crates off the shop's carpets – whereupon he invented the carpet sweeper. The 'Bissell', a mechanical device with rotating brushes, was hugely successful.

The world's first functional vacuum cleaner was invented in 1901 by the British engineer Hubert Cecil Booth. Powered by a 5hp petrol engine, it was so large and cumbersome it had to be parked on the pavement outside properties and the suction hose fed through a window. Nonetheless, Booth's device was much in demand by the upper classes and in 1902 was used to clean the red carpet in Westminster Abbey before the coronation of Edward VII. Around the same time an American, David Kenney, patented an electrically powered vacuum cleaner.

Beats as it sweeps as it cleans

Before long, handier machines began to appear. In 1907 an American caretaker named James Spangler invented a light vacuum cleaner made from an electric fan, a wooden casing and a pillowcase as a dust bag – simple but effective. His cousin William Hoover bought the patent and founded the company that would become synonymous with the vacuum cleaner. In the 20th century vacuum cleaners were steadily improved through the development of more compact motors and light, durable plastics. Machines with disposable paper bags were introduced in the 1920s, while 1979 saw the advent of the world's first bagless cleaner by the British inventor James Dyson.

ORIGINS OF THE VACUUM

The principle of the vacuum cleaner goes back to the 16th century, when the German scientist Georgius Agricola (1494–1555), in his book *De Re Metallica*, broached the idea of a ventilating fan to rid coalmines of choking dust. Several other inventors through the ages conceived similar devices, including Reverend Stephen Hales in 1741 and the Frenchmen Du Hamel and Deroux in the 19th century.

Electric power unleashed

In 1871 an obscure engineer unveiled a groundbreaking invention to the assembled luminaries of the French scientific world. The device was the dynamo, the culmination of a long process of development. It produced direct electrical current through mechanical rotation and it marked the beginning of the electric age.

History was made on 17 July, 1871, when Zénobe Gramme (1826–1901), a semi-literate Belgian cabinetmaker and self-taught electrical engineer, stood before the French Academy of Sciences to demonstrate an 'electromechanical device for generating direct current'. Gramme's machine was the first dynamo capable of generating a reliable high-voltage direct current and the end product of years of independent research by other scientists.

The story of the dynamo began in 1831 with a remarkable discovery by the British physicist Michael Faraday. He found that bringing a magnet up close to a conducting copper wire produced an electric current in the wire. The dynamo derives from this idea, being basically a device that sets magnets and wires in motion in order to produce the Faraday effect. Indeed, Faraday himself was the first to construct a direct-current generator, the ancestor of the dynamo, when he made a copper disc revolve between the jaws of a U-shaped magnet.

Growing interest

Capitalising on Faraday's principle of magnetic induction, in 1832 the Paris instrument maker Hippolyte Pixii was the next inventor to construct an electrical generator. Pixii's hand-cranked generator consisted of a U-shaped magnet (rather like a tuning fork) rotating vertically on its axis below two bobbins wound with wire to serve as induction coils. The poles of the induction coils were fixed to be opposite to the poles of the revolving magnet. As the moving magnetic field of the rotating magnet swept across the wire coils on the bobbins, they produced a current in an external circuit. But there was one major problem: during a complete revolution of the magnet, the current produced in the coil changed direction. In other words, Pixii's device generated alternating current (AC), which at the time was thought – quite wrongly – to have no

Birth of the dynamo
An engraving of 1882 (above) illustrates Faraday's famous 1831 experiment in electromagnetic induction.

Spinning magnet
The hand-cranked generator built by Hippolyte Pixii in 1832 (left) was the first practical application of Faraday's principle of magnetic induction.

THE OERSTED EFFECT

The principle behind the electromagnet is the very opposite of that of the generator – as an electric current passes through a wire, it produces a magnetic field. The effect is named after Danish scientist Hans Christian Oersted, who first discovered it in 1820.

practical use. The physicist André-Marie Ampère came up with a brilliant solution: the commutator, an electrical switch that reversed the direction of the current between the induction coil windings and the external circuit.

Vital input

Next came two key innovations by the Hungarian Anyos Jedlik in 1852–4. The first was a device that inverted the arrangement of Pixii's generator, in that the coil was now made to rotate within a stationary magnetic field. But Jedlik's real coup came in his use of electromagnets, rather than permanent magnets, to induce the magnetic field. His machine worked through the interplay between two coils: one was external and static and played the role of the electromagnet (or 'stator'), while the other, which rotated inside the first and hence is called the 'rotor', generated the current. (The complete rotating element of an electric machine, comprising both the induction coils and the metal core around which they are wound, is called the 'armature'.) This was a truly ingenious solution: when starting up, the rotation of the rotor generated a weak electric current, since the stator (even though not yet being supplied with current) produced a permanent weak residual magnetic field of its own. This weak current helped to prime the stator, which – as its magnetic field grew stronger – boosted the strength of the current generated by the rotor. The process, known as 'self-excitation', meant that some of the generator's output was constantly being used to sustain the magnetic field, while the rest was used to feed the external circuit

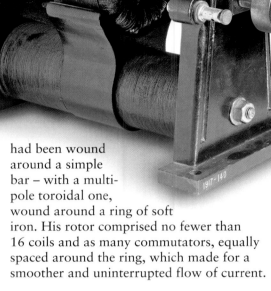

had been wound around a simple bar – with a multi-pole toroidal one, wound around a ring of soft iron. His rotor comprised no fewer than 16 coils and as many commutators, equally spaced around the ring, which made for a smoother and uninterrupted flow of current.

Electrifying industry

Gramme's dynamo improved on Pacinotti's design by having 30 armature coils and reducing the distance between the stator and the rotor. It soon went into large-scale production. Gramme flooded the market with his machines and demonstrated them at trade fairs all over Europe. Dynamo technology had come of age, and thereafter modifications to the basic configuration were minimal. Dynamos were installed in many different

Final refinements

Jedlik's machine was a major advance: the magnetic field generated by an electromagnet is far stronger than that of a permanent magnet and the result was a far greater power output. Sadly for Jedlik – a Benedictine priest – he never applied for a patent. Some years later, in 1867, generators employing self-exciting electromagnetic armatures were reinvented concurrently in Britain and Germany by Charles Wheatstone and Werner Siemens.

One further refinement to the generator was made in 1859–64 by the Italian physicist Antonio Pacinotti. He replaced the two-pole spinning coil (the rotor) – which up until then

AMPÈRE'S COMMUTATOR

Ampère's idea for rectifying the alternating current generated by Pixii's first dynamo was to position two coils in such a way that the current in each always flowed in the opposite direction to the other. The commutator comprised a metal ring mounted around the axle of the armature, which came into contact with each coil in turn as the axle revolved. As it did so, the commutator automatically changed the connection to the armature so that the magnetic field reversed, thereby producing current impulses that were all running in the same direction.

branches of manufacturing – by the 1870s, for instance, Siemens machines were powering electric arc furnaces in steelworks – and also replaced Voltaic piles in telegraph networks. The American inventor Thomas Edison modified dynamos to run his electric lighting systems. The heyday of the Gramme machine came to an end in the 1880s when industry discovered the advantages of the alternating current that had previously been dismissed.

Steam-driven dynamo
An identical machine to the one made by Edison, shown in this engraving (right), was exhibited at Crystal Palace in 1882.

FROM DYNAMO TO MOTOR

While demonstrating Gramme's dynamo at the Vienna Exposition of 1873, his colleague Hippolyte Fontaine accidentally discovered that it was reversible and could be used as an electric motor. The Gramme dynamo had been installed next to another machine that was to serve as a backup generator in case of breakdowns. But after a workman mistakenly connected their terminals together, Fontaine found that when he cranked the handle of Gramme's machine, the shaft of the second dynamo also spun round, driven by the electricity being supplied by the first.

Industrial muscle
A bank of hydroelectric-powered generators (below) installed between 1924 and 1926 to provide power for the Innwerk aluminium smelting plant at Töging in Bavaria.

Progress on display

In 1851 London witnessed two epoch-making moments: the first international trade fair and, in the course of this event, the inauguration of a telegraph link between England and France. The whole occasion was a powerful expression of how scientific advances could bring nations and peoples together. Since then, numerous international expositions have continued to showcase technological innovations and cultural diversity.

Windows on the world
A colour engraving shows the interior of Joseph Paxton's magnificent Crystal Palace, erected in Hyde Park to house the Great Exhibition of 1851.

The Great Exhibition – or, to give the event its full title, the 'Great Exhibition of the Works of Industry of All Nations' – was opened by Queen Victoria in London's Hyde Park on 1 May, 1851. It was an ostentatious display of Britain's industrial, commercial and imperial might, but it was also in effect the first world fair. More than 30 countries had accepted an invitation from Prince Albert – a driving force behind the exhibition – to stage a display of their raw materials, machinery or products, making it a truly international event. Other countries soon followed suit. France hosted an International Exposition of Agriculture, Industry and Fine Arts in 1855. London and Paris staged two further expositions, in 1862 and 1867 respectively, and Vienna entered the exhibition fray in 1873.

Cathedral of technology

The building constructed to house the Great Exhibition was a technological marvel in its own right. The Crystal Palace was the brainchild of Joseph Paxton, who had designed and built similar vast greenhouse structures at Chatsworth House in Derbyshire. It was built from prefabricated wrought-iron modules, infilled with some 300,000 sheets of glass. A special glazing trolley was designed to run along the cast iron frame of the building, enabling every glazier on the project to install an unprecedented 100 panes a day. The whole building went up in less than six months – and was dismantled when the exhibition was over for reassembly on a new site in south London.

A plethora of 'firsts'

In six months the Great Exhibition attracted 6 million visitors who flocked to see the very latest in domestic and industrial technology, including inventions from Australia, India, New Zealand and the USA, as well as from Britain and Europe. There was a precursor of the fax machine, demonstrated by Frederick Bakewell, while William Chamberlain of Sussex showed a machine for counting votes automatically. C C Hornung of Copenhagen showed his single-cast ironframe for a piano, the first to be made in Europe. On a more eccentric note, Dr Merryweather of Whitby demonstrated his leech barometer which used live leeches to predict the weather. Arguably the most influential exhibit were the flushing lavatories in the Crystal Palace retiring rooms, provided by George Jennings. It was estimated that some 827,000 people used these facilities during the exhibition and, as a result, wanted to replicate them in their own homes.

The Paris exhibition of 1855 saw such revolutionary domestic appliances as washing machines and lawn mowers. One of the stars of both Paris and London was the mechanical reaper, a prototype of the combine harvester, designed and manufactured by the American

CELEBRATING THE ENTENTE CORDIALE

Britain and France signed a defence pact, the Entente Cordiale, in 1904 and to mark the new spirit of cooperation between the old enemies, 57 hectares of farmland in Shepherd's Bush, west London, were set aside for a new joint exhibition arena. This was the venue for the Franco-British Exhibition of 1908, held in conjunction with the Olympic Games, which London hosted the same year. Exotic pavilions, many in Oriental style, were built around an artificial lake. The fair was a huge success, attracting more than 8 million visitors, and the site became known as the 'White City', from the fact that all the buildings were painted white.

Cavernous space
The Machine Hall, erected near the Eiffel Tower for the 1889 Paris Expo, became a velodrome in 1892. It was demolished in 1909.

Paris by night
A painting of 1889 (above) by the artist Georges Roux shows a view of the Trocadero Palace built for the 1878 Paris exhibition, seen through the legs of the new Eiffel Tower.

Cyrus McCormick. Twenty-five years later, the Scottish-Canadian Alexander Graham Bell unveiled the telephone at the Philadelphia Expo. The New York World's Fair of 1939 showed off early models of an appliance that would revolutionise virtually every home worldwide: the television.

Novelty value *The first 'moving pavement' appeared at the World's Columbian Exposition of 1893 in Chicago. They were still a popular attraction among a public unused to escalators at the Paris Expo of 1900 (above).*

both the Chicago World's Fair of 1893 and the 1900 Paris Expo could enjoy a bird's-eye view from huge Ferris wheels, as international exhibitions began to take on something of a fairground atmosphere – an impression compounded by the advent of electric lighting.

Pavilioned in splendour

The Crystal Palace had set the tone for the first international expos to be held in purpose-built halls, but the ambitions of the designers grew ever larger. The cavernous Palace of Industry was erected in Paris in 1855, with an imposing stone façade on the Champs-Elysées, while for the 1867 Paris fair a massive oval structure was built on the Champs de Mars comprising seven concentric galleries surrounded by a lush

Prussian pride
An illustration from Harper's Weekly *shows cannons made by the Krupp firm of Essen, Germany, on display at the 1876 Centennial Exposition in Philadelphia, the first to be held on American soil. The big guns had been used in the Franco-Prussian War of 1870–1.*

Records tumble

International exhibitions were a great boost to innovation. Manufacturers used such fairs to exchange ideas and check out the competition. Farmers were introduced to new strains of cereals and other crops, along with unfamiliar breeds of livestock and poultry. A healthy spirit of competition was fostered by a host of medals and prizes for the best products in different categories. As a natural forum for record-breaking, each international exposition tried to outdo its predecessor in size and scope. London's 1851 Great Exhibition took up 11 hectares, but the St Louis World's Fair of 1904 was almost fifty times larger. The star exhibit of the 1855 Paris exhibition was a huge stained-glass panel from the Saint-Gobain works. Thirty-four years later, the new Eiffel Tower was the main attraction. Visitors to

A NEW ART FORM

Photography truly came of age at the Paris Exposition of 1855. A huge number of submissions came from all countries and covered all genres – portraits, still-lifes, landscapes, photojournalism, even restagings of famous artworks – testifying to the popularity of photography, while the technical quality of the entries far surpassed those exhibited in London four years earlier. The organisers chose to house photography in the Palace of Industry, but the prize-giving jury proclaimed that 'The invention of Daguerre and Nicéphore Niépce is now more than just a scientific curiosity – it fully deserves to be ranked alongside the contemporary arts'.

City of dreams
An aerial view of the site for the 1900 Universal Exposition in Paris, with the Eiffel Tower standing proudly by the Seine and the large Ferris wheel also visible (in top left). A record-breaking 50 million people visited the fair, which earned 7 million francs for the French government.

Lasting legacy *The Grand Palais and the Alexander III bridge (above) were built for the 1900 Paris Exhibition.*

garden with a pagoda, a Moorish palace and a Russian log cabin. The Vienna Exposition of 1873 introduced pavilions devoted to particular sectors, rather than nations, such as farm machinery, iron and steel, or silk weaving; others were given over to individual concerns such as the Northern Railway, Bosch, Thomas Cook, Lloyd's and Krupp. In the 20th century, Expo pavilions abandoned exoticism in favour of a stripped-down modernism. At the 1958 World's Fair in Brussels, the Dutch electronics firm Philips commissioned Swiss architect Le Corbusier to design its pavilion – sadly it was torn down at the end of the event.

Another legacy of the Expos has been some striking, lavish buildings. The Great Exhibition of 1851 was a huge financial success, and Prince Albert made sure that the £186,000 profit was used to good effect. With it, he ensured the foundations of the Victoria and Albert Museum, the Science Museum and the Natural History Museum, all built in London's South Kensington. It also provided for the foundation of the Imperial College of Science, the Royal Colleges of Art, Music and Organists, and the Albert Hall, originally intended as a 'Hall of Arts and Sciences'. The Crystal Palace itself was reassembled at Sydenham in South London, where it stood until it was destroyed by fire in 1936.

The Eiffel Tower was scheduled for demolition after the 1889 Expo, but was reprieved and soon became the quintessential symbol of Paris. Other exhibition legacies include the molecule-shaped Atomium from the 1958 Brussels Expo, Seattle's Space Needle (1962), the Biosphere in Montreal (1967) and the Oceanarium in Lisbon (1998). International exhibitions have also been used as a pretext for world cities to improve their infrastructure. Thus, Paris saw the opening of its first Métro line to coincide with the 1900

Celebrating progress
In 1933 Chicago hosted a World's Fair to mark the city's centennial. It was so successful that it also reopened the following year (left).

A BRIGHT FUTURE?

The 1939 New York World's Fair was the largest ever staged. Its theme was the 'World of Tomorrow', and 44 million people flocked to see exhibits presenting a vision of utopian cities, futuristic consumer products and fast, convenient transport. The centrepiece was a complex of two ultra-modern buildings called the Trylon, a spire-like structure, and the Perisphere, a dome housing a model of a city of the future – visitors viewed it from above on a moving walkway. Another highlight was the General Motors 'Futurama' exhibit, which showed a diorama of life in America as it might be in 1959, with automated highways and sprawling suburbs. The railroad section featured streamlined locomotives. When the fair reopened for its second season, in 1940, it was without the Czech and Polish pavilions, as their countries had been invaded by Germany. But despite the war, many of the fair's optimistic projections did come to fruition.

SHOWCASING THE ARTS

Sculpture and the Fine Arts was one of the four 'divisions' of the Great Exhibition (the others being raw materials, machinery and manufactures). It was a mecca for the applied arts rather than fine art and the very latest work in virtually any medium was on display, including ceramics, clocks, fountains, glass, jewellery, leatherwork, lighting, metalwork, mirrors, musical instruments, sculpture, textiles and wallpaper. By contrast, painting was given prominence in the Paris Exposition of 1855, with pride of place going to *The Empress Eugenie Surrounded by her Ladies in Waiting* (1855) by the Emperor's favourite court portraitist, the German Franz Xaver Winterhalter. The work of the Neoclassicist Ingres and the Romantic Delacroix – two titans of the art world – was displayed, while the leading light of the Realist school, Gustave Courbet, filled an entire pavilion. Parisians were also much impressed by the work of the English Pre-Raphaelites, such as Edward Burne-Jones.

Thereafter art became a permanent fixture at Expos. Yet in the main, truly innovative artists whose works have since stood the test of time found it hard to gain a foothold. Japanese art, which was to have a major influence on Impressionism, was first introduced to the West at the 1862 exhibition in London. The chief exponents of Impressionism, such as Manet, Monet and Cézanne, were exhibited at the Paris

1889 Exhibition, but it was completely forgotten conservative academicians – like Meissonnier and Bouguereau (who signed a petition against the building of the Eiffel Tower that year) – who were best represented and carried off the prizes. Lovers of the avant-garde had to seek out works by groundbreaking artists in the more far-flung sections of the fair. These included Gauguin, the American painters Whistler and John Singer Sargent, and artists from the radical new Symbolist movement, such as the Swiss Ferdinand Hodler, the Belgian Félicien Rops, the German Franz Stuck and the English artists Edward Burne-Jones and John Everett Millais.

The applied arts fared well from exposure at international exhibitions – many works from the Great Exhibition remain on display at the Victoria and Albert Museum. After seeing work by the French glassmaker Emile Gallé and by the Nancy school at the Paris Exposition of 1878, the American Louis Comfort Tiffany was inspired to take up the art form. In turn, his own 'favrile glass' was much admired at Paris in 1900, where Art Nouveau was all the rage. Increasingly, creativity in later eras focused on the architecture of the pavilions. The building that became the model for this trend was the modernist pavilion created by the German Bauhaus architect Mies van der Rohe for the 1929 Barcelona Expo.

Style icons
The German pavilion at the Expo '29 in Barcelona was designed by cutting-edge architect Mies van der Rohe. It was demolished at the end of the fair, but in 1983–6 a replica was built on the same site (below). In the foreground is the architect's MR90 'Barcelona' chair in chromed steel and leather. The chair became an instant design classic, imitated by others ever since.

Brave new world
With China poised to become the world's leading industrial nation in the 21st century, Shanghai staged Expo 2010 as a celebration of the country's growing confidence and booming economy.

Space age
The Century 21 Exposition staged in Seattle in 1962, during the presidency of John F Kennedy, looked optimistically to the future. Its centrepiece was the 182-metre high Space Needle, with its flying saucer-like viewing platform, which still dominates the city.

Exhibition. Montreal used the 1967 Expo to extend its underground network beneath the St Lawrence River and to create an innovative housing development (Habitat 67). For the 1992 Expo in Seville the city expanded west to reconnect with the Guadalquivir River, which had been diverted many decades before.

Ulterior motives

Many international exhibitions have pursued or reflected political agendas. In the 19th century, for example, European powers used them to strengthen their grip on their colonies. At the 1937 Paris exhibition, the pavilions of the Soviet Union and Nazi Germany faced one another in symbolic expression of the growing confrontation between the two countries.

Above all, Expos are about national self-image. Philadelphia celebrated the centenary of the 1776 US Declaration of Independence, while the 1889 Paris Expo commemorated the French Revolution. The World's Columbian Exposition of 1893, also known as the Chicago World's Fair, marked the 400th anniversary of the discovery of America by Columbus. The 1970 Osaka Expo marked Japan's emergence as an economic superpower. Seville '92 confirmed post-Franco Spain's future in Europe. Hanover 2000 was the first fair held in a reunified Germany. Expo 2010 in Shanghai, whose slogan is 'Better city, better life', is set to mark China's growing importance in the world.

Cool, fresh food

Traditional methods of preserving food – such as salting, smoking, drying or immersing in oil – worked well enough, but they radically altered the flavour of the food. Ice could keep food fresh but quickly melted. The invention of the refrigerator revolutionised people's kitchens and eating habits.

Chilly conditions
Workers at an ice storage warehouse, drawn by the German artist Aloys Eckhardt in 1895.

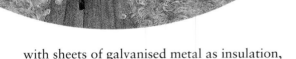

with sheets of galvanised metal as insulation, in which the food sat directly on a block of ice that was replaced every week or so.

Pioneers of refrigeration

Research was already well underway on artificial means of refrigeration. It had first been demonstrated in 1748 by William Cullen at the University of Glasgow, then in 1805 the American Oliver Evans designed the first refrigeration process to use a vapour instead of a cooled liquid. In 1834 the American inventor

Curious contraption
An ice-cutting machine on the St Lawrence River in Canada c1900. Blocks of ice from Canada were exported all round the world for the conservation of foodstuffs.

The earliest ancestor of the modern refrigerator was widely used by the ancient Mesopotamians, Greeks and Romans. Foodstuffs and liquids to be preserved were placed in a shallow pit filled with ice or snow, then covered with a thick layer of insulating straw to keep the cold in and slow down the melting process. Throughout Europe from the 17th century onwards, especially on estates serving large country houses, cold pits were supplanted by purpose-built brick icehouses. Where appropriate, the ice was brought from nearby hills and mountains, or cut in winter from nearby lakes or rivers. A thriving trade in ice began in Europe during the 1700s and by the early 19th century it had developed into a major industry. By that time, large blocks of ice were being shipped from the United States and Canada. In the 1850s the first small ice-chests began to appear in the USA, before being adopted in Britain and the rest of Europe. An ice chest was a small wooden cabinet, lined

THE COWBOYS' SWANSONG

From the early 1860s, the growth of cities across the USA boosted the demand for beef. In Chicago, Cincinnati and other Midwestern cities, the stockyards and slaughter-houses were working at full capacity. In 1867, in the town of Abilene, Texas, at the end of the Chisholm cattle trail, a major railhead was developed for the export of livestock to cities on the Eastern seaboard. That same year saw the introduction of the first refrigerated railroad cars. From 1878 to 1881 the Swift Company, owners of the largest meat-packing plant in Chicago, established a sophisticated meat distribution network involving refrigerated boxcars and local branches with cold stores. This sounded the death knell for the epic cattle-drives run by cowboys in former decades, which had passed into history by the 1890s.

Cold in the hold
Two engravings, first published in the Illustrated London News *in 1877, show two views of cold storage on the refrigerated British freighter* Victoria. *On the left are carcasses hanging in the refrigeration plant; on the right, blocks of ice in the ship's cold store.*

REFRIGERATION SHIPS

Before the advent of artificial refrigeration, it was impossible to transport perishable goods by sea on voyages that in some cases could last for months. In the spring of 1868, French engineer Charles Tellier installed a small experimental cold store on a ship bound for Argentina. The cargo arrived at its port of destination in perfect condition, but the Academy of Sciences in Paris failed to recognise the achievement until 1874. Tellier set about repeating his experiment, this time purchasing and equipping a steamer, which he christened *Le Frigorifique*, with proper refrigerated holds. He set out from Rouen for Buenos Aires in 1876, but a pump failed and the cargo was spoiled.

The next year, Ferdinand Carré made the same journey in the other direction. Sailing from Buenos Aires in the *Paraguay*, which he had fitted with refrigerators that could chill meat to –30°C, he arrived in Le Havre with his cargo of mutton intact. In 1879 refrigerated shipping from the USA to Britain was pioneered by the *Circassia*, and the *Strathleven* inaugurated the route from Melbourne to London in 1880, but it was the clipper *Dunedin*, the first vessel to bring frozen lamb to Britain from New Zealand in 1882, that marked the beginning of commercial success for refrigerated ships. By the end of the century, more than 350 refrigerated ships were plying the world's oceans.

The well-equipped home kitchen
The 'Kleen-Kold' refrigerator (left) was one of the earliest fridges to be developed for the American domestic market. It appeared in the 1920s.

Jacob Perkins lodged the first patent for a practical refrigeration machine, which he described as an 'apparatus and means for producing ice'. In Perkins' device a gas (ethyl ether) was compressed by an air pump, and the heat of the compression was removed by passing the fluid through a coil immersed in water. The ether was allowed to expand through a valve into a chamber near the bottom of a cistern of water, so the low temperature produced by the evaporation of the expanding ether was transmitted to the surrounding water. The basic principle of the refrigerator was thus established, but ether was both highly flammable and odourless, a lethal combination at a time when candles and oil lamps were the standard forms of lighting.

In 1857 a French engineer by the name of Ferdinand Carré built a refrigeration machine based on the expansion of ammonia gas. Two years later, he patented a system without a compressor – it worked instead through the continuous absorption of ammonia. In 1863 another French engineer, Charles Tellier, invented a system that used methyl ether as the refrigerant; this new gas was less prone to form an explosive mixture at high pressure than the earlier chemicals used.

Food on the move

Tellier and Carré were also instrumental in fitting out ships with refrigeration units. In 1877 the steamer *Paraguay* made history when she carried a refrigerated cargo from Buenos Aires to France. Three years later, the first frozen mutton from Australia was unloaded at London Docks. In 1881 meat-packing companies in the USA began using refrigerated railway cars to transport meat from the stockyards of Chicago and Kansas City. As cities expanded and the demand for meat began to outstrip supply from local farms, refrigeration became a vital element in the food distribution chain. With the increased availability of imported food from abroad, people could eat fruit and vegetables out of season and diets changed accordingly.

The industry surrounding the transport and preservation of meat was crucial to the growing Australian population and in 1857 Australian James Harrison developed the world first practical ice making machine and refrigeration system. This was subsequently used in the meat-packing and brewing industries. In the early 1870s German chemist Carl von Linde revived the compression of ammonia to develop refrigerators that found an instant market with German brewers.

Revolution in the home

The first practical domestic refrigerator was made in Chicago in 1913. Called the Domelre (short for 'Domestic Electric Refrigerator'), it stood over 2.5 metres high and was powered by a primitive electric motor mounted on top

FREON COLD

Dangerous refrigerants like ammonia and methyl chloride were replaced in 1929 by a new substance called Freon, which was non-toxic, non-corrosive and non-flammable. As a chlorofluorocarbon (CFC) compound, freon was later found to be harmful to the Earth's ozone layer and was itself replaced by tetrafluoroethane.

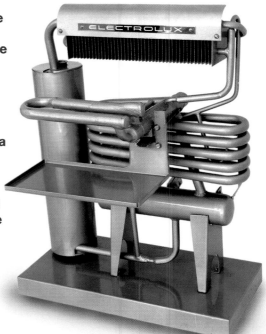

of the cabinet. Improved machines for the home were produced by Kelvinator in 1918, Frigidaire in 1919 and Electrolux in 1925. By 1939, half of all homes in the USA had a fridge. Home freezers were introduced in 1960, enabling people to store deep-frozen food for months on end. Widespread fridge and freezer ownership boosted the food processing and packaging industries. Foodstuffs, even fresh items, were packaged to keep better under refrigeration, while ready-cooked meals that only needed to be taken from the fridge and reheated grew in popularity.

Cooling system
An Electrolux absorption refrigeration unit from the 1960s (above). The Electrolux company began making fridges in 1925.

Cold storage in waiting
A refrigerator warehouse in the UK in 1957. Fridges are now the most popular domestic electrical appliances in the world.

DEEP FREEZING

Slow freezing ruins foodstuffs because the formation of large ice crystals breaks down the cell structure. In around 1915, the American naturalist Clarence Birdseye discovered that if food was dipped in salted water before being frozen by an icy wind, it emerged in a much better state when it was defrosted. As a result of this rapid deep-freezing, the ice crystals in the food were smaller and less damaging. Birdseye then designed a machine that could quick-freeze food on a moving belt chilled by a refrigerant. In 1930, in conjunction with the General Foods Company, he developed a successful range of frozen foods for the retail market, notably frozen peas and fish.

A place for everything
In addition to the usual shelving, modern fridges have temperature-controlled compartments suited to different types of food. Fridges are often now combined with freezers, and some even have automatic ice-cube makers.

HOW FRIDGES WORK

In refrigerators that use a *compression* system, the refrigerant is vaporised in pipes that run around the inside of the machine. As the liquid evaporates, it draws in the ambient warmth. The vaporised liquid is compressed by a pump (the compressor) that re-circulates it to a condenser located outside the fridge. Because the refrigerant is under high pressure, it instantly condenses back to liquid, giving off heat that is dispersed into the air by the vanes at the back of the machine. After passing through a pressure-release valve, the liquid is pumped back into the evaporation pipes inside the fridge and the cycle begins again.

In an *absorption* refrigerator, the refrigerant (usually ammonia) is vaporised by a heat source (a naked flame or an electric element). The resulting gas is then dissolved in a liquid (water) which has the effect of cooling it down and condensing it. The absorption of the ammonia by the water changes the pressure in the pipes, and this causes the refrigerant to circulate of its own accord without the need for a noisy compressor. Small units of this type powered by liquid petroleum gas (LPG) are widely used in motor-homes, for example.

A new rhythm in the office

When the typewriter made its first appearance in the late 19th century, it was a cutting-edge piece of technology epitomising the fast pace of life and work in the new industrialised world. A century or so later it disappeared, replaced by the computer.

Rudimentary writer
A model replica of an early typing device patented by Sholes, Glidden and Soule in 1868 (right). It bore little resemblance to later typewriters.

Leading brand
A poster from 1910 by Italian designer Leonetto Cappiello (below) advertising Remington, at the time the world's leading typewriter manufacturer.

For most of the 20th century, offices everywhere resounded to the incessant clacking of typewriters. The first typing pools date from the early 1900s, but the question of who invented the machine itself is less certain. When the first mass-produced typewriters went on sale in 1874, made by the Remington Company of Ilion, New York – a company and village already famous for its rifles and sewing machines – there were no fewer than 52 similar inventions in existence. The Remington typewriter was an improved version of a design patented by Carlos Glidden, Christopher Latham Sholes and Samuel W Soule in 1868.

First steps

On 7 January, 1714, London engineer Henry Mill was granted a patent for what might well be the world's first typewriter. All that is known for certain about Mill's machine is the claim in the patent that it could produce letters 'so neat and exact as to not be distinguished from print'. The following century, attempts to produce a typewriter came thick and fast – from Americans Charles Thurber (1843), Oliver T Eddy (1850) and Alfred Ely Beach (1856), and from the French symbolist poet Gérard de Nerval (1854).

Sensing the lucrative market that would soon open up, inventors tried circumventing the patent to promote the virtues of their own machines. New forms of rapid communication such as trains, the electric telegraph, offset rotary presses and the telephone were already a reality. But while telegraphists and stenographers could key up to 130 words per

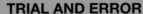

Remington

TRIAL AND ERROR

Christopher Latham Sholes was born in 1819 and served an apprenticeship as a printer before becoming a newspaper editor. A strike by compositors prompted him to attempt to design a typesetting machine, but it was a failure. In 1866, along with fellow printer Samuel W Soule, Sholes began work on a machine for paginating books. A friend, the lawyer Charles Glidden, suggested that it might also be used to produce letters and words. The following year an article in *Scientific American* described a prototype typewriter, known as the 'Pterotype', made by the English inventor John Pratt.

Sholes and Soule resolved to make a less complex, more practical version of Pratt's machine, with Glidden supplying initial funds. They patented their invention in 1868, then approached John Densmore for financial backing, who agreed in return for a quarter-share in the patent. Densmore rejected their first prototype, prompting Glidden and Soule to quit. Sholes and Densmore soldiered on through an exhaustive series of tests and modifications. After 50 attempts, they had a workable machine to present to Remington. The company bought the patent, paying Sholes $12,000 for his stake. Densmore held out for a royalty agreement instead – a shrewd move that made him a millionaire.

QUERTY ET AL.

Sholes and Soule's first prototype could be described as like a piano for writing with. Its flat keyboard comprised two rows of keys (black and white), with the letters arranged alphabetically. Yet the clashes between the typebars that could occur when several keys were struck in quick succession often caused jams. Accordingly, Sholes decided to space out the most commonly used letters so they would not clash. In 1874 he patented a keyboard with four rows of keys: the now-famous 'Qwerty' arrangement in which the word 'typewriter' can be typed on the top line – a boon to salesmen. The first version did not include the numbers 0 and 1, as it was thought that the capital letters 'O' and 'I' could substitute. Other arrangements competed for a while, but Qwerty was adopted as the industry standard in the early 20th century. August Dvorak patented the 'American Simplified Keyboard' in 1934, claiming it was more ergonomic than the traditional layout, but it failed to catch on. Each country developed its own variation on the Qwerty layout to suit the requirements of the language: thus, French-speaking countries have Azerty, Germany has Qwertz and Italy Qzerty. And though the typewriter has now all but disappeared, Qwerty lives on in computer keyboards.

minute, no-one could write at a rate of more than 30 words a minute (a world record established in 1853).

The first Remington enjoyed a modest success, with 1,200 machines sold, but it was heavy, expensive and difficult to use. Later improved models sold like hot cakes. The same was true of rival machines, notably those manufactured by Underwood. Various innovations improved on the basic design. The shift bar, for example – introduced on the Remington No 2 in 1878 – allowed typists to switch almost effortlessly between upper and lower-case letters. A major step forward came in 1887 when both the Columbia Barlock and Oliver models enabled typists to see what they had typed (on earlier machines the typebars struck upward against the bottom of the roller, or 'platen', so people were typing 'blind').

By the turn of the century, a standard configuration had established itself: a keyboard, die-cast metal characters on typebars worked by levers, and a movable carriage on rails holding both the paper and an inking device (generally a ribbon).

From electric typewriters to computers

Using a typewriter required strong fingers, and it was not long before manufacturers came up with the idea of using small electric servo motors to make the typist's task easier. In 1902 the Blickensderfer Manufacturing Company, which in 1893 had marketed the first portable typewriter, introduced the Blick Electric, but in

Number One
The Underwood No 1 typewriter, introduced in 1896, quickly established the company's reputation. Among other innovations, it was the first machine to have tabs, enabling column widths to be set precisely and to be justified.

The typing pool *A typical scene in a US firm in the 1930s. From the 1920s onwards, many women started their working career in the typing pool and worked their way up through the secretarial ranks.*

THOROUGHLY MODERN TYPISTS

When typewriters first came into widespread use in the later 19th century, society was extremely conservative. Middle-class women who dared to go out and earn a living were looked upon almost as fallen women. The founder of the first secretarial college, Miss Helen White, came close to being publicly lynched. Things slowly improved in the 20th century. Secretaries were often well-educated young ladies from good families who made a conscious choice to go out to work to assert their independence. Novelists and playwrights helped to popularise the figure of the efficient young working woman about town. Machine manufacturers were the first to organise typing classes, later augmented by night classes run by local authorities, professional or commercial bodies, or specially run training schools. The boss and his secretary/typist now became the basic unit of the office workplace. In the early 1980s, with the arrival of the computer and word-processing software (then later e-mail), people found they could write their own correspondence. A century after shorthand-typists first appeared in the workplace, they were consigned to history.

Lady typist *A young Victorian lady working on her typewriter.*

COMPLEX TASK

The first machine that could type Chinese characters was not produced until 1949. It had a bank of 72 keys, which could reproduce all of the language's 43,000 different pictograms.

the absence of a widespread and reliable electricity network, the machine was a flop. (It did, though, give rise to teleprinters, used for sending urgent messages.) The 1920s brought the first real success for the electric typewriter. The American inventor James Fields Smathers, who had produced a prototype machine in 1914, approached the Northeast Electric Company in 1923 with a plan for an electric-powered Remington. In 1928 Delco, a subsidiary of General Motors, took over Northeast and began to market Smathers' typewriter as the Electromatic. Five years later, when International Business Machines bought the firm, it became the IBM Electromatic.

The first of IBM's own machines came in 1935, and they set the standard for the rest of the market. Their famous Selectric typewriter, in which the characters were printed by a rotating ball while the carriage stayed fixed, was introduced in 1961. Yet just as typewriters reached a peak of development in the 1970s and early 1980s, they effectively heralded their own demise. Equipped with internal memory and external memory-storage devices, and able to type on reams of continuous printout paper, this final generation of typewriters represented the beginnings of word processing. They prefigured the personal computer, which steadily supplanted typewriters from the early 1980s onwards.

ALTERNATIVE ARRANGEMENTS – THE MIGNON, THE GOLF-BALL AND THE DAISYWHEEL

The arrangement on typewriters that became standard from around 1910 onwards was a keyboard with one key per character, each at the tip of its own separate typebar. Yet radical new designs were around even in the early days of the typewriter. The German 'Mignon' index typewriter, which was manufactured from 1903 to the eve of the First World War, had just a single key and a typesleeve containing a complete set of characters. The operator simply moved a stylus to point at the desired letter displayed on an index card and pressed the key. In 1893 the American George C Blickensderfer devised a machine with one key per letter, but with the characters set on a rotating disc rather than individual typebars. This made the 'Blick' typewriter much lighter and more portable and the machine was a great success, even going into an electric version, well ahead of its time, in 1902. It was also the inspiration behind the electric-drive IBM 'golf ball' machines, popular in the 1960s and 1970s, which had fixed carriages and revolving typeballs. In the later 1970s, the golf ball was supplanted by the daisywheel, a thin plastic disc with the letters moulded on the outer rim of the 'petals'.

New versatility
The most innovative feature of IBM electric typewriters was the interchangeable 'golf ball' (top), which enabled the typist to switch between different fonts.

Office revolution
The IBM 72 Selectric typewriter (left), introduced in 1961, revolutionised the office. The electric drive meant that it took a far lighter touch to activate the keys, while the whole machine weighed just 14 kilograms.

The birth of modern archaeology

In 1874, three years after he first broke ground at the site of the ancient city that Homer had described so memorably in his epic poems, the self-taught German archaeologist Heinrich Schliemann published *Trojan Antiquities*. This seminal work marked the beginnings of pre-Hellenic archaeology.

Man on a mission
Heinrich Schliemann sketching the remains of the southeastern gate of Troy in 1882 (below). The illustration is taken from Troja, Results of the Latest Researches, *a work published in London in 1884 by Charles Darwin's publisher John Murray.*

In 1870, after having recently arrived in Greece, where he hoped to locate the sites described in Homer's *Iliad* and *Odyssey*, Heinrich Schliemann (1822–90) decamped to Turkey. There he began excavations at Hisarlik, a small hillock overlooking the Dardanelles, not far from the coastal town of Çannakale. The hill had been identified as early as 1822 as a possible site for ancient Troy, and by the time Schliemann arrived, a British amateur archaeologist, Frank Calvert, had been excavating there for almost 20 years on land owned by his brother. Calvert showed that Hisarlik was at least in part man-made, comprising successive layers of ruins.

Schliemann became convinced that this was Troy. The ancient city was described in the *Iliad* as sitting between two rivers on a broad plain – the Scamander and the Simois – and here the hill was indeed flanked by two rivers.

Mycenean masterpiece
A replica of the Mask of Agamemnon, found by Schliemann at Mycenae in 1876. The original is in the National Archaeological Museum in Athens.

Schliemann made preliminary soundings, followed by seven full seasons of digging from 1871 to 1890. He also excavated at the Greek sites of Ithaca, Tiryns and (from 1874) Mycenae where, in 1876, he discovered a shaft grave near the 'Lion Gate'. This was found to contain several gold artefacts, including the celebrated 'Mask of Agamemnon'.

Troy rediscovered

At Hisarlik, Schliemann was so eager to verify Homer's account and get at the stratum he believed to be contemporaneous with the destruction of the city by the Greeks, he dug straight down through the top layers of the site, destroying their archaeology. His first major find – a relief of the sun-god Apollo, once part of a frieze in the Temple of Athena – came from the Hellenistic period that followed the death of Alexander the Great in 323 BC.

Eventually Schliemann worked out that there were no fewer than four earlier cities beneath the ruins of the Graeco-Roman settlement of Ilium, the last town to be built on

the site. In May 1873, during his third season of digging, he came across a fortress on the second level that he declared to be the palace of King Priam. A 7-metre wide entranceway came to light which he dubbed the Scaean Gates, through which the defenders had dragged the Trojan Horse. He also unearthed a vase on which he thought were traces of Trojan script and an owl's head representing the goddess Athena. His greatest find was a magnificent hoard of copper, silver and gold artefacts that he christened 'Priam's Treasure'

A controversial figure

The discovery of Priam's Treasure secured Schliemann's fame and in 1877 he and his second wife Sophie were even made honorary members of the exclusive Society of Antiquaries in London. Yet the authenticity of the treasure was questioned by scholars in both Paris and Berlin, who speculated that it might have been cobbled together from various artefacts found at different locations around the site. It turned out that some pottery he had claimed dated from the supposed time of the fall of Troy (*c*1250 BC) was in fact at least 1,000 years older. Later research brought to light not five but nine cities at Hisarlik, dating from prehistoric times to the early Roman Empire. Troy VII (the different strata are designated by Roman numerals) corresponds with the city described in the *Iliad*, or at least with its acropolis. (Excavations in 2001–2 by a team from the University of Tübingen revealed the presence of a surrounding settlement from the same period – Troy VIIa – built on lower ground that was 13 times larger.)

At least Schliemann was humble enough to acknowledge some of his mistakes. His colleague Wilhelm Dörpfeld persuaded him to change his destructive digging methods and adopt stratigraphy instead – the technique of clearing away the soil from a site layer by layer in order to study the different archaeological strata.

A born adventurer

By the time he started work at Troy, Heinrich Schliemann had already led a colourful life, including some rather shady episodes. The son of a Protestant minister, he started his working life as an apprentice to a grocer, before becoming a book–keeper in Amsterdam. He then landed a position with an import/export firm and

Exquisite artefact
A replica of a golden pin dating from 2600 to 1900 BC (below right), which formed part of Priam's Treasure.

The second Mrs Schliemann
Sophie Schliemann, photographed in 1882 (below), wearing some of the golden jewellery found at Hisarlik.

pursued a prosperous career as a trading agent in Russia. He fell from grace in St Petersburg after being accused of fraud and next resurfaced in Sacramento, California, founding a bank that lent money to gold prospectors. Around this time, he became a US citizen and bought land in Cuba. By now he had learned several languages – he would eventually speak 13, including his native German – and became a restless globetrotter, living briefly in Sweden, Denmark, India, China and Japan. By 1866, Schliemann was resident in Paris, earning a living as a property speculator and attending classes in Egyptology and Sanskrit at the Sorbonne. A journey to Rome and Naples

SPOILS OF WAR

Priam's Treasure has been the subject of controversy ever since Schliemann took it away from Troy without the knowledge of the Turkish authorities. It was transported to Germany in 1881 and displayed at the Pergamon Museum in Berlin. When the city fell to the Red Army in 1945, the hoard disappeared. It resurfaced again in 1993, after the collapse of the Soviet Union, in the reserve collection of the Pushkin Museum in Moscow. While legal wranglings over ownership continue, a replica of the treasure is now displayed at the Neues Museum in Berlin.

kindled his interest in ruins. His one true passion since childhood had been the history and mythology of ancient Greece. In 1869 he divorced his Russian wife Ekaterina (they had been married since 1852) and married a Greek woman, Sophia Engastromenos, who bore him two children, Andromache and Agamemnon.

For all his archaeological ambition, Schliemann also had an acquisitive side; when Priam's Treasure came to light, rather than share it with the Turkish authorities who had granted him excavation rights, he spirited it away to a grand mansion he had built for

Compelling myth
In a scene from the 2004 film Troy, *directed by Wolfgang Petersen, the Wooden Horse is dragged within the city walls by Troy's defenders (above). The besieging Greeks, under the command of Agamemnon, built the horse to smuggle their soldiers into the heart of the city. The frieze detail showing the siege of Troy (above right) is from a sarcophagus now in the Ashmolean Museum, Oxford.*

Commanding view
A reconstruction of Troy VI painted by Peter Connolly in 1986. This incarnation of the city was destroyed by an earthquake in c1300 BC .

himself in Athens. There, surrounded by frescoes celebrating his work, he revealed the hoard to the world's press. Schliemann was always adept at managing the media. His dispatches to *The Times* often embellished the truth; his claim, for instance, that Sophia smuggled Priam's Treasure out of Hisarlik by wrapping it up in her shawl rides roughshod over the fact that she was not even present on the site when the cache was discovered.

Towards a scientific discipline

Wilhelm Dörpfeld went to work for Schliemann in 1882, having made his name on the excavations at Olympia under the auspices of the German Archaeological Institute of Athens, founded in 1873. Such scholarly institutions proliferated in the 19th century – the Istituto di corrispondenza archeologica in Rome (founded 1829), the French School of Athens (1846), the French

Ahead of his time
Photographed in Egypt in 1878 (right foreground), the French archaeologist Auguste Mariette (1821–81) opposed the plunder of archaeological sites and promoted conservation of artefacts in the lands where they were discovered.

High tech analysis
Ion beam analysis apparatus – like this equipment (below) in the Louvre Museum in Paris – allows scientists to study the materials of which artefacts are composed without inflicting damage.

Cairo Institute (1879) – and played a key role in organising archaeological digs, which spread beyond the Graeco-Roman world. As early as 1839 John Stephens, an American, had set off in search of the ancient Mayan civilisation, while the French scholar Paul-Émile Botta began excavating the site of Khorsabad in northern Iraq in 1843. Gradually, archaeology became a rigorous scientific discipline. Stratigraphy, first developed in geology by the Englishman William Smith, was popularised in archaeology by the French pioneer Jacques Boucher de Perthes (1788–1868). Finds were dated by comparing them with remains from other sites, which allowed scientists to identify similarities and then build up a relative chronology.

Dating was later refined through chemical and other scientific forms of analysis. Fluorine absorption dating, for example, measures the fluorine content of fossilised bones to determine how long a corpse has been in the ground. Radiocarbon dating was introduced by the American physical chemist Willard Frank Libby in 1945. Modern archaeology is making increasing use of palynology – the analysis of spores and pollens – which reveals much about ancient farming and eating habits and the different stages of occupation of a site. Likewise dendrochronology, which analyses the growth rings in trees, has become valuable. Other modern techniques include geophysical and aerial surveying, which can reveal subterranean structures invisible at ground level, DNA analysis (showing population movements) and forensic facial reconstruction.

Jeans
1873

In 1847 an 18-year-old German Jew named Löeb Strauss left his native Bavaria and emigrated to New York. There he went to work in a wholesale dry goods business owned by his brothers, Jonas and Louis, who had come to America some time before. Soon after, Löeb took the forename Levi. In 1853 the bright prospects offered by California during the Gold Rush prompted Jonas and Louis to send Levi out to San Francisco to set up and manage a West Coast branch of the family business. Once established, Levi Strauss & Co quickly expanded and Levi became a prominent and respected figure in the city.

Trademark rivets

One of Levi Strauss's regular customers, a Latvian-born tailor named Jacob Davis, ran his own business making workwear. To solve the problem of pockets tearing, in 1872 he began reinforcing the corners with copper rivets. Davis suggested he and Strauss go into partnership, and they patented their distinctive denim trousers on 20 May, 1873. Manufacture of the famous 'Model XX' jeans, renamed Levi 501s in 1890, began in San Francisco under Davis's supervision. Hard-wearing and practical, they were an instant hit with miners, cowboys and farmers. The huge earthquake and fire that devastated San Francisco in 1906 destroyed the factory, but Levi Strauss & Co rose from the ashes and has since become a major multinational concern.

Leader of the pack
Films like The Wild One *(1953, director Laszlo Benedek), starring Marlon Brando as the leader of a motorcycle gang (left), popularised jeans as a symbol of rebellion.*

A FABRIC CONQUERS THE WORLD

Contrary to popular myth, the first blue jeans were not made from tarpaulin cloth but from the same denim fabric that is still used today. Denim is named after the city of Nîmes in the south of France, which manufactured a serge cloth made from silk and wool that was much in demand throughout Europe, including in England, from Renaissance times onwards. Around the same time, sailors from the city-state of Genoa in Italy took to wearing rugged trousers woven from another type of serge (a mixture of wool and linen). This material was also imported by garment makers in England, where it presently became known as 'jeans' after its city of origin. By the late 18th century, both fabrics were being produced in England using cotton imported from colonies of the British Empire. Denim was woven from a coloured warp with a white weft, whereas the weave of jeans material was uniformly coloured. Denim proved the more durable of the two and became the fabric of choice for workwear. When Levi Strauss started making his famous blue jeans in America, he used a home-produced denim.

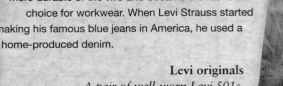

Levi originals
A pair of well-worn Levi 501s.

FERTILISATION – 1875

The secrets of the human egg

T he German zoologist Oskar Hertwig was the first person to observe the process of fertilisation. His investigations into how eggs developed – a subject that for centuries had been shrouded in myth – helped to promote the new science of embryology.

Ideal choice

An electron microscope photograph of a sea-urchin egg ten minutes after being fertilised (blue image, top right) is far more detailed than the image Hertwig had at his disposal in 1875. Yet even his relatively crude equipment enabled him to observe the process of fertilisation, a major breakthrough in the history of the life sciences.

In 1875, while studying reproduction in sea urchins, the 26-year old scientist Oskar Hertwig was able to observe through his microscope, for the very first time, the act of fertilisation taking place. At the time, he and his brother Richard, another brilliant zoologist who was one year his junior, were both working at the University of Jena. Oskar made his momentous discovery while on a field trip to Ajaccio on the island of Corsica. Hertwig's professor at Jena, the renowned German zoologist and philosopher Ernst Haeckel, was on the same trip. Years later, he paid homage to his former student's work in *The Riddle of the Universe* (1901): 'The beautiful capital of the island in which Napoleon the Great was born, in 1769, was also the spot in which the mysteries of animal conception were carefully studied for the first time in their most important aspects.'

Oskar Hertwig's own description of the experience displays the intellectual rigour that became his stock-in-trade: 'I was fortunate enough to be able to demonstrate: (1) that a few minutes after having mixed the sperm with the mature eggs, the head of a spermatozoon appeared in the cortical layer of the vitellus ... and that it presently transformed into a small corpuscle, which I shall call the spermatic nucleus; (2) that several minutes later an act of copulation could be observed between the egg nucleus and the spermatic nucleus; and (3) that in the normal course of events only a single spermatozoon is involved in the fertilisation process.' Although Hertwig had not observed the actual penetration of the spermatozoon into the oocyte, he was the first to provide incontrovertible proof that sexual

THE FERTILE SEA URCHIN

A s far back as 350 BC, Aristotle remarked upon the extraordinary fertility of the sea urchin, which can produce millions of eggs a year. In the 19th century, this marine invertebrate became a favourite subject among researchers investigating reproduction. In addition to their great abundance, large size and rapid development, sea urchins also had the enormous advantage of being transparent, which made observation of their functions more straight-forward. Recent advances in developmental and molecular biology have corroborated the choice of the sea urchin as an ideal study model.

union between a male and a female is a vital element for reproduction in most species.

Ovists versus spermatists

Hertwig's observations placed the matter beyond all doubt: fertilisation came about through a fusion between the nuclei of the male and female gametes. At the time, the recognition that cells of both sexes played an equal part in the process was a real eye-opener. Ever since Aristotle, author of the first work on embryology in the 4th century BC, some extremely far-fetched theories had been advanced regarding the development of the embryo and the respective roles played by the male and female in its formation.

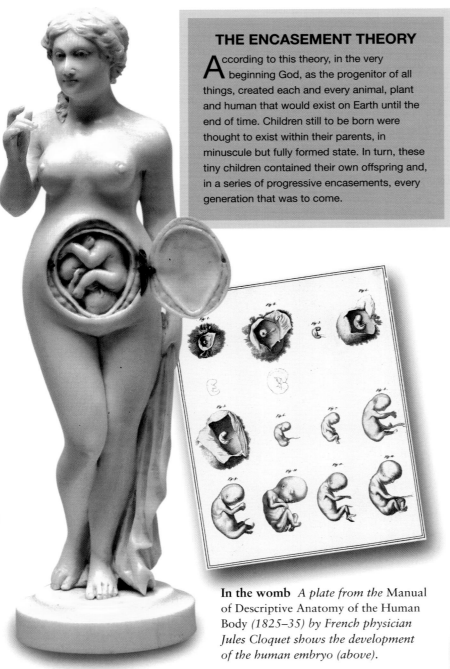

THE ENCASEMENT THEORY

According to this theory, in the very beginning God, as the progenitor of all things, created each and every animal, plant and human that would exist on Earth until the end of time. Children still to be born were thought to exist within their parents, in minuscule but fully formed state. In turn, these tiny children contained their own offspring and, in a series of progressive encasements, every generation that was to come.

In the womb *A plate from the* Manual of Descriptive Anatomy of the Human Body *(1825–35) by French physician Jules Cloquet shows the development of the human embryo (above).*

Origins of life
An 18th–19th century anatomical model of a pregnant woman, carved in ivory. A 'door' in the abdomen is hinged and opens to show the position of the foetus within the uterus.

From the 17th century onwards, exponents of a theory known as preformationism maintained that the embryo was a tiny creature already fully formed in the womb, right down to the minutest detail. But even within this school of thought there were two factions who disagreed over the origins of the embryo. According to a group known as the ovists, the embryo came from the egg; in contrast, the animalculists (or spermatists) contended that it derived from the male sperm.

The Dutch microbiologist Antonie van Leeuwenhoek, who was the first to observe spermatozoa through a microscope in 1677, belonged to the latter camp. In 1694 the Dutch scientist Nicolas Hartsoeker produced a sketch of a 'homunculus', a miniature individual huddled inside the head of a spermatozoon. Five years later, under the pen-name of Dalempatius, the French astronomer François de Plantade claimed to have seen a minuscule human with perfectly formed arms, legs, torso and ahead emerging from a spermatozoon.

Many scientific scholars – ovists and animalculists alike – subscribed to the theory of encasement, which held that progressively smaller embryos were stacked inside one another, rather like Russian dolls, such that all generations were present from one original creation. Taking this idea to its logical conclusion, this meant that the whole of humanity – past and future – was already contained in the ovules of Eve and the spermatozoa of Adam.

Future generation
A drawing of a foetus in the womb (below), from the second edition of Ernst Haeckel's Anthropogeny, or the History of Human Evolution *(1891).*

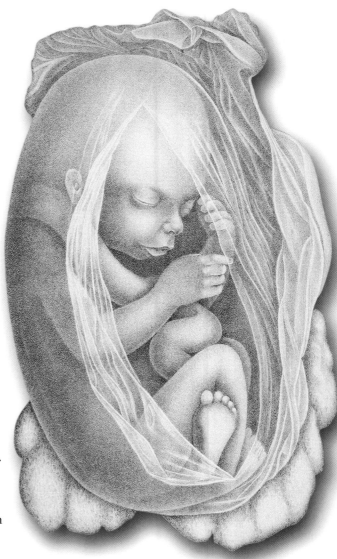

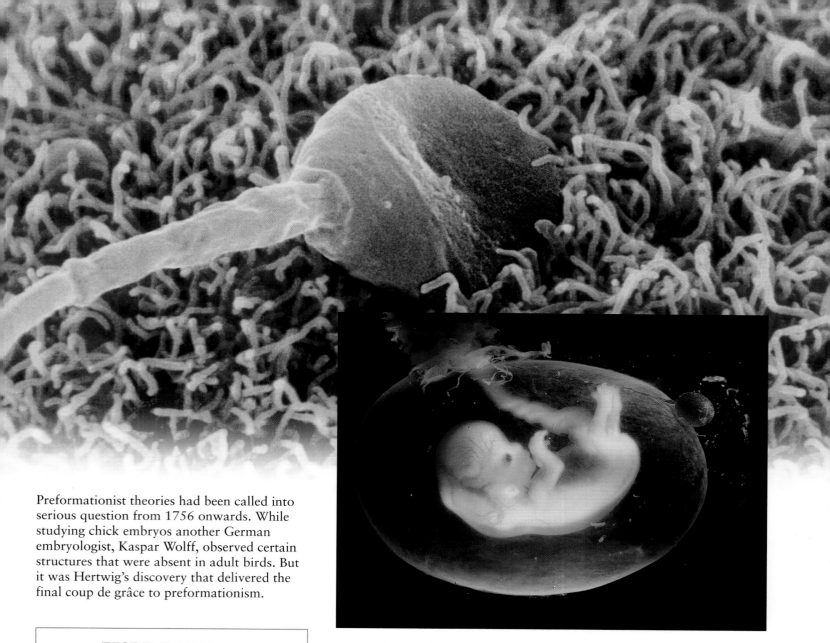

Preformationist theories had been called into serious question from 1756 onwards. While studying chick embryos another German embryologist, Kaspar Wolff, observed certain structures that were absent in adult birds. But it was Hertwig's discovery that delivered the final coup de grâce to preformationism.

TEST-TUBE BABIES

The world's first test-tube baby, Louise Brown, was born in Britain in 1978. Since then, in-vitro fertilisation (IVF), which is offered to couples who are experiencing difficulties in conceiving, has resulted in the birth of millions of children worldwide. In the classic form of IVF treatment, the growth of eggs in the ovaries is stimulated hormonally, then they are removed to be fertilised by the male's sperm in a fluid medium. This culture medium is placed in an incubator at 37°C. Two or three days later, the resulting fertilised eggs – in today's practice, two at most – are implanted in the woman's uterus.

Doctors are also able to inject sperm directly into an egg. This technique, which is called ICSI – intracytoplasmic sperm injection – was first used in 1991 in Brussels. It increases the chances of successful fertilisation taking place and is also able to overcome certain forms of male sterility for which classic IVF treatment is of no use.

Founding fathers

At the same time other German researchers such as Heinrich Wilhelm von Waldeyer-Hartz and Theodor Boveri were beginning to push back the boundaries of biological knowledge by describing mitosis, cell division leading to the creation of two identical cells. Little by little, the mysteries of fertilisation and formation of the ovule were being unravelled by science. This laid the essential groundwork for the emergence in the early 20th century of embryology as a discipline in its own right, studying the development of the foetus on a cellular, molecular and genetic level. As one of the first to foresee the role played by heredity and to describe chromosomes, Hertwig was a founding father of genetics. His work, and that of his successors, led to many invaluable practical applications in medicine, most notably artificial insemination, which nowadays account for 2 per cent of all births in developed countries.

Revealing reproduction
Technological advances such as scanning electron microscope (SEM) images and computerised tomography (CT) scans have allowed scientists to probe the innermost secrets of the reproductive process. These images show a spermatozoon (top) attempting to break through the wall of an ovum in order to fertilise it, as seen through an electron microscope, and a scan (above) of a 7–8-week-old foetus in the womb.

Bell sets the world talking

The world's first telephone call was made by Alexander Graham Bell on 10 March, 1876, from his laboratory in Boston. Ringing his assistant, who was waiting by a receiver on the floor above, the inventor solemnly uttered the words: 'Mr Watson, come here, I want you!' Thomas Watson heard the message loud and clear; the age of the telephone had dawned.

Prototype phone
A model (above) of the apparatus used by Alexander Graham Bell in his 1875 experiments in transmitting sound. The engraving (top right) shows the very first telephone call from Bell to his assistant Thomas Watson, which took place on 10 March, 1876.

In some ways, the advent of the telephone seemed long overdue. For centuries, inventors had dreamed of recording and reproducing the human voice, though not of transmitting it over distance. English physicist Robert Hooke conducted the first experiment in producing a sound wave of known frequency in 1667. In 1782 a Cistercian monk by the name of Dom Gauthey presented to the French Academy of Sciences his idea of exploiting the acoustic properties of tubes. The following year, this long-distance speaking system was successfully tested in Paris over a distance of 800 leagues (almost 2.5 miles). The telegraph, an early version of which came into use in 1793, quickly caught the imagination. Over the course of the 19th century it revolutionised international trade and diplomatic communications. Yet it never found its way into people's homes, nor indeed most offices. By the late 19th century, the pressing need for a direct and instant method of communication began to become apparent, particularly in the world of business.

Early experiments

From the 1850s onwards, inventors in various countries latched on to the concept of the telephone. One early pioneer was Charles Bourseul, a lowly employee in the telegraphic bureau of the Paris Stock Exchange, who on 26 August, 1854, wrote in the periodical *L'Illustration*: 'Suppose that a man speaks near a movable disc sufficiently flexible to lose none of the vibrations of his voice; that this disc alternately makes and breaks the currents from a battery: you may have at a distance another disc that will simultaneously execute the same vibrations.' Bourseul here outlined the basic principle of the telephone, and it only remained to put the idea into practice. Unfortunately for Bourseul, the French authorities were not blessed with foresight and refused to back his proposal. Many people remained sceptical about the feasibility of the concept.

Inspired by Bourseul's article, in 1861 a German schoolteacher named Johann Philipp

HOOKE'S TELEPHONE

The English scientist Robert Hooke (1635–1703) has many claims to fame: he formulated a law, named after him, concerning the elasticity of solid bodies, and he also anticipated the wave theory of light. In 1667 he gave a public demonstration of an attempt to transmit sound vibrations over distance. His apparatus comprised two boxes with flexible bottoms, set some 200 metres apart and linked by a piece of taut string. The experiment worked well: two people were able to converse over the distance without raising their voices. Hooke's device, which later became a familiar children's toy, was effectively a mechanical telephone, although the term itself (from Greek *tele*, meaning 'far', and *phone*, meaning 'sound') would not be coined until 1796. The megaphone and the speaking tube – widely used in mansions to summon servants from distant rooms – worked on the same principle.

Reis used a device he called a 'telephone' to transmit musical tones played by orchestral instruments over a distance of 100 metres. Yet while Reis could reproduce music with a fair degree of accuracy, he found it impossible to convert electrical current back into distinct human vocal sounds. Despite various attempts, Reis failed to create a fully working telephone and died, aged just 40, in 1874.

Bell and his patent

Other 19th-century inventors, such as Antonio Meucci and Elisha Gray, conceived of the idea of using electricity to transmit the human voice by converting sound waves into electrical pulses. The only one among them to become a household name was Alexander Graham Bell who, in February 1876, lodged a patent for 'the electro-magnetic transmission of vocal sound by undulatory electric current'. As Bell himself conceded, the apparatus in question 'did not … produce very satisfactory results'.

On 2 June, 1875, while conducting tests with an acoustic telegraph to try to send several messages on the same line, he heard the overtones of a steel reed that his assistant Thomas Watson had mistakenly plucked at the other end of the line. In subsequent experiments, Bell found that he was able to transmit speech electrically, but that the individual words were indistinct. It did not take him long to improve his telephone. To compensate for the weakness of the electrical current produced, he replaced the magnets in the transmitter with a metal wire immersed in a solution of sulphuric acid. In June 1876 he demonstrated his telephone to a large audience at the Philadelphia Centennial Exposition. The following year Western Union refused Bell's offer to sell the company his patent outright.

WRONG CALL

In 1876, after using Bell's device to contact Philadelphia, US president Ulysses S Grant declared: 'It is an astonishing invention. But who on Earth would ever want to use a telephone?'

A CLOSE-RUN THING

On 14 February, 1876, the electrical engineer Elisha Gray lodged his patent for a telephone with the US Patent Office just one hour after Bell had submitted his. Gray, a 41-year-old professional inventor from Highland Park, Illinois, had first dreamt up the idea of the telephone two years before. He and Bell – who was 13 years his junior – had a very similar conception: a harmonic telegraph that could transmit multiple messages down a single wire at the same time. They were aware of each other's work, but by 1875 Gray was certain that his rival was barking up the wrong tree: 'As to Bell's talking telegraph, on which he seems to be expending all his energies, it will only create interest in scientific circles. Its commercial values will be limited … I have no intention in these circumstances of wasting my time and money on an enterprise that is doomed to failure from the outset.' So he turned his attention elsewhere, until one fateful day when he saw children playing with a can-and-string telephone, and it dawned on him that the electric telephone was a brilliant idea. Too late; a fortnight after filing his patent Bell wrote to his father: 'This invention is my work through and through and it is sure to bring me fame, fortune and success.'

The next year, Bell's rival Thomas Alva Edison perfected the telephone by adding a carbon microphone. This consisted of two metal plates separated by granules of carbon; as the pressure on the granules changed, so did the electrical resistance between the plates, increasing the volume of the voice. Bell acquired the patent for this device from Western Union in 1879, and not long after the telephone made its debut in the United States and Europe. London was linked to Paris in 1891 and to New York in 1927.

Ringing in a new world

The telephone heralded momentous social change. Many people considered the telephone a great boon. Yet others deplored the way it violated social conventions. Formerly, anyone wishing to gain admittance to a respectable household had to leave their calling-card. Now all and sundry could call unbidden. The telephone also gained a bad reputation for enabling young men to whisper sweet nothings to the objects of their affection without being overheard. Well brought-up young ladies were instructed never to pick up the receiver.

To begin with, telephones were confined to the homes of the very rich. Even in Germany, where they caught on fastest, there were only 52 telephones per 1,000 inhabitants in major cities like Berlin and Hamburg. At first, telephones were leased in pairs to subscribers, who had to arrange for a telegraph contractor to run a line between them. Then came central telephone exchanges: to connect with another person, the subscriber had to be put through by an operator. In the very early days,

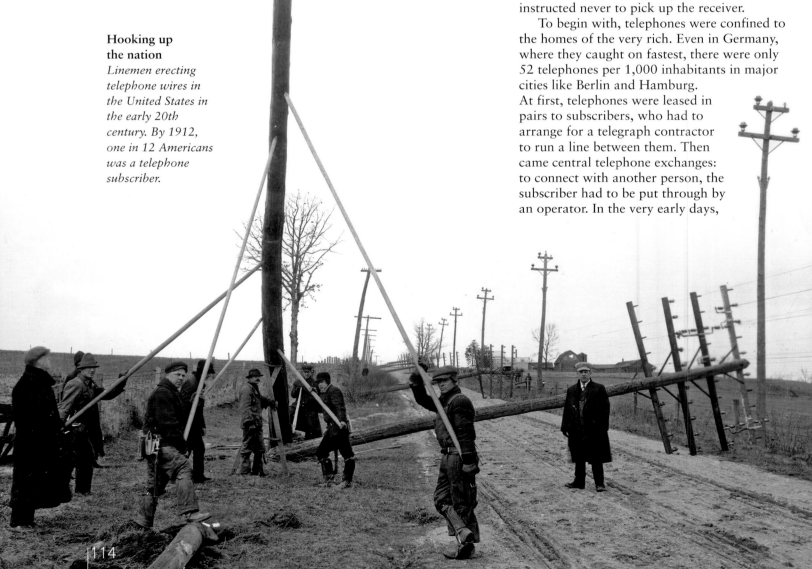

Hooking up the nation
Linemen erecting telephone wires in the United States in the early 20th century. By 1912, one in 12 Americans was a telephone subscriber.

Putting you through *A telephonist at the Volkswagen plant at Wolfsburg in the 1930s (far right). Operators at telephone exchanges could connect up to 400 calls every hour.*

Direct dial *The 1905 Strowger 11-digit telephone (right), which allowed people to call directly. The telephone dial was invented by Almon B Strowger.*

Big-screen potential *It was not long before the telephone made its appearance in films. Comedians like Stan Laurel (left) exploited its comic possibilities.*

A TIRELESS INVENTOR

Bell's other inventions include an air-conditioning system, a hydrofoil boat and various unsuccessful heavier-than-air flying machines. He built the world's first metal detector in 1881, in a failed bid to locate an assassin's bullet in the body of **US President James Garfield.**

the operators were all single young women hand-picked for their refined voices, good manners and discretion. But as the number of subscribers continued to increase and the demand for telephonists grew, some less scrupulous operators began to eavesdrop on private conversations. Kansas City undertaker Almon B Strowger introduced the 'girl-less, wait-less' automatic exchange in 1889. It came about because he suspected a local operator of intercepting his clients and redirecting them to her husband's funeral parlour. Now callers had no need to go through an exchange. They could simply dial the number and a system of electromagnets would connect them.

A RIVAL CLAIMANT

On 11 June, 2002, the US House of Representatives formally recognised Antonio Meucci as the real inventor of the telephone. This Italian-American conceived his 'talking telegraph' in 1854, some 16 years before Bell. Born in Florence in April 1808, Meucci first made a name for himself in his home town as a theatre technician. He emigrated to America in May 1850, where his first invention was an ingenious device that transmitted sound from the bedroom of his wife, who was crippled with rheumatoid arthritis, to his office. In 1860 a New York journal published details of the apparatus, but Meucci did not patent it for lack of funds. As a result, he was overtaken by Bell, whose first job was in a laboratory where the prototype of Meucci's 'talking telegraph' had been installed. Meucci died in 1896 but almost a century later, in 1989, Basilio Catania, former director of the Italian Telecommunications Research and Development Agency (CSELT), made it his task to have Meucci recognised as the telephone's rightful inventor. On 1 May, 2000, a major step was taken when the Mayor of New York, Rudy Giuliani, inaugurated Meucci Day to mark the 150th anniversary of his arrival in the city. Yet despite the 2002 judgment, many historians of technology still do not recognise the claim.

Phone evolution
A hand-crank telephone of 1910 (right), mounted in an oak stand. The U43 telephone (below), manufactured by Ericsson in 1943, had a shell made of Bakelite, an early plastic.

Stop press
Public telephone booths first appeared in the 1880s. They were a godsend to journalists like these correspondents (below), pictured in Washington in 1942, who could ring through stories to their papers, reporting news virtually as it happened.

FROM EARPIECE TO KEYPAD

Groundbreaking though the invention was, the actual telephone apparatus devised by Bell was not very practical as the receiver had to be constantly shifted between the mouth and the ear. It was replaced in 1892 by the wall-mounted telephone, but the first of these were scarcely more efficient: the user spoke into a receiver while holding an earpiece to the ear and at the same time had to crank a handle to call the operator. The handset telephone first appeared in 1910; an easy-to-hold handset combined an earpiece at the top and a microphone at the base. Then, with the advent of the automatic exchange, came a dial for the caller to select the number they wanted. Up to the First World War, most telephone subscribers were wealthy and the sets were fashioned accordingly as elegant home furnishings of hardwood and brass. Standardisation came with the introduction of the Ericsson U43 in 1943, the first telephone to be made of Bakelite. Telephone design then remained virtually unchanged until the advent of the modern keypad phone in the 1980s.

Yet the automatic exchange had one major flaw. Along a single telephone line, the speaker's voice would fade rapidly. Beyond 2 miles, the listener could not hear a thing. To solve this problem, in 1906 the American inventor Lee DeForest devised the amplifier vacuum tube, or triode. Thereafter lines became longer, linking ever more distant cities. In 1956, a telephone cable was laid under the Atlantic.

Telephones became more common in the 1930s, but it was the postwar period, especially the 1960s onwards, when they came to be installed in almost every office and home. The phone facilitated both business transactions and social contacts. People could now call friends and relatives in far-flung parts of the globe. It brought a radical change to arranging leisure time, and eventually to the way people worked, with the introduction of teleworking and videoconferencing. The communications revolution gathered pace with the appearance of new technologies such as the fax machine, the videophone and the Internet. Nowadays, the fixed telephone landline, which took so long to become a reality, is steadily being supplanted by the mobile phone.

Ancient meets modern

Brazilian Caiapo Indians use a phone booth at Kari Oca, on the outskirts of Rio de Janeiro, during the World Conference of Indigenous Peoples on Territory, Environment and Development, held in the city in May 1992.

SUPERPOWER HOTLINE

During the Cuban Missile Crisis at the height of the Cold War in 1962, the world stood on the brink of nuclear war, yet during that vital 13 days there was no direct communications link between the United States and the Soviet Union. It took at least 12 hours for the Americans to receive and decode messages sent by Russian premier Nikita Khrushchev. Accordingly, on 20 June, 1963, the superpowers met in Geneva and agreed to install an emergency telephone link between the White House and the Kremlin to facilitate communication to defuse potentially dangerous situations. But contrary to popular myth, there is no 'red telephone' sitting on the President's desk in the Oval Office. The first US-Soviet 'hotline' was a simple telegraph link running from the Pentagon. To aid détente, a similar hotline was established between the USA and China in November 2007.

ALEXANDER GRAHAM BELL – 1847 TO 1922

A life in sound

Alexander Graham Bell's main claim to fame was his invention of the telephone, but this Scottish emigrant to Canada then America spent only 15 years of his long life on the idea. His wider interest in sound transmission led him to investigate the acquisition of language and in particular the causes of deafness.

Alexander Graham Bell was born in Edinburgh on 3 March, 1847, into a family of gifted linguists. Both his grandfather and father were renowned experts on phonetics and elocution. His father, Professor Alexander Melville Bell, even devised a method of 'visible speech' designed to teach the deaf how to speak. This involved symbols showing the position and movement of the tongue, throat and lips when producing particular sounds. His mother was afflicted by deafness. Both of Alexander's brothers died of tuberculosis, after which the family emigrated to Canada in 1870, moving to the United States the following year.

In 1872 Bell founded a school for the deaf in Boston and in 1873 he was appointed professor of Vocal Physiology and Elocution at the city's university. His aim was to perfect the vocal training of the pupils in his care. In 1872 he made the acquaintance of Gardiner Greene Hubbard, a prominent and wealthy lawyer with business interests in a telegraph company. Bell started teaching Hubbard's deaf and mute daughter Mabel and began work on a machine that would help her to hear. Hubbard lost no time in pledging his financial backing to the young researcher.

Self-made man

At the age of 29, Bell unveiled his 'harmonic telegraph'. The following year, 1877, he founded the Bell Telephone Company together with Hubbard and his assistant Thomas Watson. He also married Mabel Hubbard and during his honeymoon to Europe presented his invention to Queen Victoria. In all, Bell spent four years promoting his invention at home and abroad.

By 1880 Bell was wealthy enough to retire from business life, yet he had no intention of putting his feet up. He took US citizenship in 1882 and shortly after became a member of the American Academy of Sciences. He financed the journal *Science* and was a founder member of the National Geographic Society. As well as fighting two important legal cases to protect his rights as an inventor, he also

ALEXANDER AND MABEL

Bell first met Mabel Gardiner Hubbard (1857–1923) in 1872, when she was 15. A bout of scarlet fever at the age of 5 had left her both deaf and mute. Bell was asked to help her regain the power of speech. The couple fell in love and were married in July 1877. Although he was ten years her senior, Mabel outlived her husband by only a year.

Crude apparatus
A prototype of the telephone made by Bell in 1876 (above).

Family portrait
Alexander Graham Bell and his family photographed in c1885. His wife Mabel was almost certainly one of the first to test the prototype of a hearing-aid invented by Bell in 1874. The device incorporated a sheet of glass coated with lamp black, which picked up sounds.

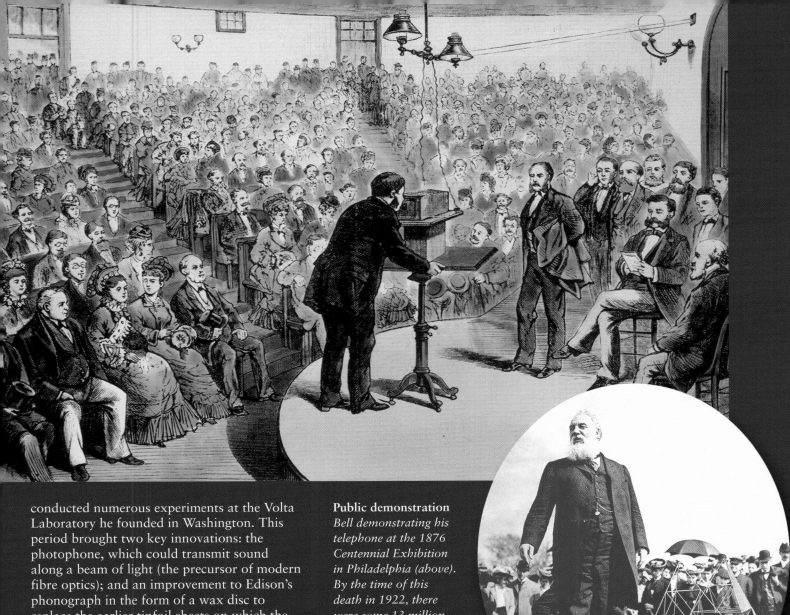

conducted numerous experiments at the Volta Laboratory he founded in Washington. This period brought two key innovations: the photophone, which could transmit sound along a beam of light (the precursor of modern fibre optics); and an improvement to Edison's phonograph in the form of a wax disc to replace the earlier tinfoil sheets on which the sound was recorded. He experimented with kites and other flying machines, and even got involved in sheep rearing as a way of studying the causes of hereditary deafness.

Conquering deafness

Throughout his career, Bell's chief concern was with problems of hearing in general and in particular teaching deaf people how to speak. More than half of the hundred or more papers he published were on this subject. He spelt out his preoccupation with deafness in a letter to his wife: 'There is one thing which I grow more certain of with every day that passes, and that is that my concern for the deaf will last my entire life. There remains so much to do but so few people qualified to do it. I shall never abandon this work, and you may be sure that whatever success, pecuniary or otherwise, I may enjoy elsewhere in life, your husband will always be known as an educator of deaf-mutes or at least as someone who had their interests at heart.' Alexander Graham Bell died in Nova Scotia on 2 August, 1922, aged 75.

Public demonstration
Bell demonstrating his telephone at the 1876 Centennial Exhibition in Philadelphia (above). By the time of this death in 1922, there were some 13 million telephones worldwide.

Flying machine
Alexander Graham Bell photographed in 1904 with his Tetrahedral Kite, a revolutionary design that was light and stable in flight. Bell also experimented with heavier-than-air flying machines.

BELS AND DECIBELS

The bel (B) and the decibel (dB, a tenth of a bel) are units of measurement employed in the fields of acoustics, physics and electronics. They were named in honour of the inventor of the telephone and adopted in 1927. They are relative units: in other words, it is essential to state the frame of reference by adding an abbreviation. For example, dB SPL (sound pressure level) signifies the degree of acoustic pressure relative to the lowest level perceptible by the human ear, while dB HL (hearing level) measures the hearing of a person relative to a base figure of zero, which denotes normal hearing.

119

THE PHONOGRAPH – 1877

Captured for posterity

It is generally agreed that the first machine to record and reproduce sound was constructed in 1877, but there remains some dispute as to who first invented it: the American Thomas Edison or the French poet and engineer Charles Cros.

Sound research

In Léon Scott de Martinville's phono-autograph of 1856 (above right), sound waves emitted by a large tuning-fork were engraved onto a rotating drum.

Fast work

A replica of the first tinfoil phonograph (above), reputedly made in just 30 days by Edison's brilliant Swiss-American machinist John Kruesi.

On 30 April, 1877, Charles Cros deposited a sealed envelope at the Academy of Sciences in Paris containing a short note headed 'Process for recording and reproducing phenomena perceived by the sense of hearing'. In it, he described the workings of an ingenious machine he had constructed and christened the 'Paleophone' (from Greek, literally meaning 'a voice from the past'). Cros' device took its inspiration from the so-called 'phono-autograph' apparatus built by the inventor Léon Scott de Martinville 21 years earlier. As a human voice was directed at the machine, it caused a diaphragm to vibrate, which in turn inscribed a trace on a rotating drum coated with lamp-black. This trace was then transferred by means of photo-gravure onto a metal disc, creating grooves. When connected up to a receiving diaphragm, the contours of the grooves reproduced the original sound. Cros wrote a poem entitled 'Inscription' describing the grand design behind his invention. Roughly translated, it read:

'Like the features in a cameo
I wanted lively gestures
To be a treasure, kept forever
Able to repeat the dream
Music of the fleeting hour
Time seeks to flee, and I subdue it'.

On 10 October, 1877, a French journalist first used the term 'phonograph' (Greek for 'sound writing') to describe Cros's invention. Cros eventually secured a patent in 1878.

Overnight sensation

Meanwhile, on the other side of the Atlantic, Thomas Alva Edison was also hard at work trying to capture and reproduce sound. In a diary entry from 18 June, 1877, he noted: 'I am in no doubt that I shall soon succeed in

A POET AMONG SCIENTISTS

Charles Cros was born near Carcassonne, in the southwest of France, on 1 October, 1842. He was an exceptionally gifted child, reading Latin and Greek by the age of 8 and mastering Hebrew and Sanskrit by 11. He enrolled on a medical course but gave it up to become a poet and freelance scholar. At the Paris Universal Exposition of 1867, Cros unveiled a plan for an automatic telegraph system. In 1868 he sent a proposal to the Academy of Sciences for a photographic colour process, but he failed to patent his process and it was another Frenchman, Louis Ducos du Hauron, who went down in history as the originator of colour photography in 1868–9. Some of Cros's ideas were highly fanciful, such as his plan to communicate with other planets using mirrors, or his scheme to chemically synthesise precious stones. He frequented Bohemian circles in Paris – his friends included the poets Verlaine and Rimbaud – and his own writing anticipated Surrealism with its strong sense of absurdity and irony. He also wrote extended humorous monologues for a famous comic actor of the age. In later life he took to drink, dying in poverty and obscurity with most of his work unpublished. The Charles Cros Academy continues to commemorate his life and work by awarding prizes for the best recordings of the year in France.

120

making an automatic and perfect recording and reproduction of the human voice.' On 22 August, Edison sent a drawing of a piece of apparatus to his associate, the machinist John Kruesi, with the terse instruction: 'Kruesi, make this.' Edison's sketch showed a horn acting as both a microphone and loudspeaker. This was linked to a steel needle attached to a diaphragm that vibrated from top to bottom when spoken into. The recording surface was a sheet of tinfoil wrapped around a clockwork-driven metal cylinder that had a spiral groove running from one end to the other. As the sound entered the horn, it caused the needle to vibrate; as this ran along the groove, the embossing point made deeper or shallower indentations in the foil, depending on volume.

To listen to this analogue recording (in which sound is captured in a form analogous to the vibration, as opposed to digital recording where it registers as a sequence of numbers), another diaphragm-and-needle unit for playback was hooked up to the horn.

Music machine
America was amazed by Edison's phonograph and soon his workshops were turning out attractive production models with metal horns and wooden cases. Record cylinders, precursors of vinyl discs, were stored in colourful boxes.

All that was then required was to rotate the cylinder once more. The steel needle, ancestor of the diamond-tipped stylus on a modern turntable, traced the hollows and bumps in the tinfoil, causing the membrane to vibrate and the recorded sound to emerge from the horn.

Within weeks, Edison's prototype was ready. The inventor cranked the handle and began singing a popular nursery rhyme into the recording diaphragm: 'Mary had a little lamb, its fleece was white as snow …' He then mounted the cylinder on the playback unit and there was his own voice squawking the tune

The master's voice
A photograph of 1899 shows Thomas Alva Edison recording his own voice. Edison's advertising proclaimed: 'I want to see a phonograph in every American home.'

back at him. The sound was distorted and weak, but perfectly intelligible. Edison later confessed 'I've never been so surprised in all my life!'. Anticipating commercial success, he registered his invention with the US Patent Office in Washington on 24 December, 1877. Word quickly spread and soon journalists were beating a path to Edison's research laboratory at Menlo Park, New Jersey, to marvel at his machine. Public demonstrations were organised and enthralled audiences the length and breadth of the country. US Congressmen and even President Rutherford B Hayes came in person to listen to the new phonograph.

Edison's ten suggestions

In June 1878, in an article published by the *North American Review*, Edison listed ten probable uses for his invention. Music only appeared in fourth place. In abridged form, the list was as follows: (1) *Dictation*: the writing of letters and all manner of dictation with no need for a stenographer; (2) *Books*: phonographic books that would 'speak' to blind people, or even to 'the lady or gentleman whose eyes and hands may be otherwise employed'; (3) *Elocution*: as an elocutionary aid or as a primary teacher for children;

(4) *Music*: 'a song sung on the phonograph is reproduced with marvellous accuracy and power'; (5) *Family records*: for preserving the sayings, voices and the last words of dying members of the family and of great men; (6) *Application in other devices*: allowing, for example, musical boxes to emit human voices or toy locomotives 'to be supplied with their natural and characteristic sounds'; (7) *Clocks*: 'The phonographic clock will tell you the hour of the day, call you to lunch, send your lover home at ten, etc'; (8) *Speech and other utterances*: 'It will henceforth be possible to preserve for future generations … the voices of our Washingtons, our Lincolns, our Gladstones, etc'; (9) *Educational purposes*: 'by it difficult passages may be rendered for the pupil only once, after which he has only to apply to his phonograph for instructions'; (10) *Perfecting the telephone*: 'Were our telephone-conversation automatically recorded … it would be expressly resorted to as a means of perfect record.'

Collector's item

By the early 1900s, gramophones were becoming attractive objets d'art to grace the homes of the well-off. This model (left), made in 1906 by the Gramophone and Typewriter Co, had a striking blue horn and an elegant wooden case. The turntable was rotated by a spring-driven motor, which was wound up manually with a handle.

Live recital

A soprano performing at the Beethoven Hall in Berlin, accompanied by an orchestra made up entirely of gramophones. The performance was recorded visually in this coloured wood engraving after a drawing by Friedrich Gehrke in 1899.

ORIGIN OF AN ICON

One the most famous and enduring images from early gramophone history is Nipper, the Jack Russell terrier who is pictured listening intently to a gramophone horn in the registered trademark of His Master's Voice (HMV). The name and image was copyrighted to The Gramophone Company, founded in 1897 as a British partner to Emile Berliner's US Gramophone Company. Bristol-based artist Francis Barraud had originally painted his dog Nipper in front of an Edison cylinder phonograph. He offered the image to the Edison-Bell Company, but was curtly informed that 'Dogs don't listen to phonographs'. So he took his picture to the rival firm, who accepted it on condition that a Berliner disc gramophone was substituted for the original apparatus.

Yet the technological shortcomings of the phonograph doomed to failure attempts to exploit it as a business machine. The sounds recorded on a cylinder, for example, could only be replayed a few times at reasonable quality. It was also necessary to turn the handle constantly throughout the recording. The phonograph, it seemed, was fated to be a plaything and object of curiosity.

Birth of the record

Edison embarked on his famous experiments in electric lighting and suspended work on 'Mr Phonograph', as he called his earlier invention. The next major innovations in sound recording and reproduction came from the engineers Chichester Bell (a cousin of Alexander Graham Bell) and Charles Sumner Tainter. Together, they built a 'graphophone', which had an electric motor, a floating stylus and cylinders made from cardboard covered with a durable wax coating that was more hardwearing than the earlier tinfoil versions. The sound quality was far superior to Edison's machine. Edison responded by buying out their patent in 1885.

That same year, Emil Berliner, a German émigré to the USA, devised a process for creating a master disc. This involved engraving a zinc template to a constant depth by chemical means. Using the template, copies of

HOME OF THE CLASSICS

The German record company Deutsche Grammophon (DG), a favourite label for lovers of classical music, was founded in November 1898 by the brothers Joseph and Emile Berliner. They believed strongly in the social and historical importance of sound recordings. One of the earliest artists whom they captured for posterity was the legendary Italian tenor Enrico Caruso. By 1904 DG was pressing 25,000 records a day and had a catalogue of more than 5,000 titles. From the late 1970s, digital re-mastering helped to revive many 'lost' historic recordings. The famous yellow label continues to be the home of some of the world's most renowned classical performers.

Shared experience
The phonograph was a source of wonder in the early days of sound recording. In the 1890s entrepreneur Lloyd C Mitchell set up a parlour in Salina, Kansas, where for a small fee passers-by could drop in and listen to recordings.

The crowing cockerel
The French firm Pathé, later to become famous for its cinema newsreels, helped to establish the recording industry in France. Pathé began in 1896 by marketing a phonograph inspired by Edison's machine. They expanded into pressing records in 1905. This 78rpm disc (right) from the 1910s has the famous cockerel logo on the label and sleeve.

All that Jazz *The gramophone quickly became associated with the free-and-easy attitude of the Jazz Age of the 1920s and dance crazes like the Charleston and Black Bottom. This image of a young woman enraptured by gramophone music was taken by French photographer René-Jacques in 1927.*

A GHOSTLY VOICE FROM THE PAST

In 2008, using digital technology, researchers at the Lawrence Berkeley National Laboratory in California brought to life a phonoautogram recorded 148 years earlier by the French engineer Léon Scott de Martinville. The original recording – the world's oldest known soundtrack – was made on a sheet of paper coated with lamp-black. De Martinville's phonoautograph equipment was only capable of recording sound, not playing it back, but after digital restoration a faint female voice could be heard slowly but distinctly intoning the words of the famous folk song 'Au Clair de la Lune'.

the original recording could be turned out in small production runs. The same year Berliner unveiled the 'Gramophone', a turntable for playing recorded discs. Soon, he improved his system by inventing a method of stamping out records in a more durable material – a hard rubber called vulcanite. This marked the birth of the 78rpm disc and standardised speeds, which before then varied from 60 to 130rpm.

Among early celebrities invited to record their voices for posterity were Queen Victoria, Florence Nightingale and William Gladstone. Yet gramophones and phonographs remained prohibitively expensive. Few people imagined that recorded music would one day outstrip live performances in popularity. A foretaste of the future came with the first gramophone recording of a concert, Handel's oratorio *Israel in Egypt*, at the Crystal Palace in 1888.

From the 78 to downloads

The spread of the gramophone was boosted when 78s began to be made from shellac rather than vulcanite (which produced an irritating background hiss). Records began to be reproduced in their thousands. The number of recordings increased every year, as the price of gramophones and discs continued to fall. By the 1920s, more than 60 per cent of all British homes had a gramophone.

A major advance came in 1925 with the invention of electric amplification of sound. Then in 1948 the 33rpm long-playing record was devised by Peter Karl Goldmark for the Columbia Record Company. This new format

SPECTACULAR GROWTH

Records first became mass-market consumer goods in the 1930s. But it was growing prosperity after the Second World War that really caused record sales to skyrocket. Record companies in the USA, for example, saw their profits treble between 1946 and 1960.

Teen turntable
The development of new plastics in the 1960s made it possible to produce light, portable record players (below) that the growing teenage market could afford.

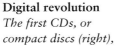

New style
From the 1930s, old horn-style gramophones began to be replaced by more portable models with loudspeakers mounted in the lid. This compact machine was manufactured by His Master's Voice.

Digital revolution
The first CDs, or compact discs (right), were made by Philips and Sony in 1979, barely a century after the first phonograph cylinders.

WORLD OF MUSIC

In total, it is estimated that some 40 billion records – 78s, LPs, singles and CDs – have been bought since 1877.

could hold almost six times more music than the old shellac 78s, which it soon supplanted. Other landmarks were the introduction of stereophonic sound and multitrack recording in around 1965, and the emergence of CDs in the digital revolution of the 1980s.

The rise of the Internet, the craze for the Walkman and more recently the iPod and the digital home studio have all helped to confirm the central role that recorded music plays in most societies. Yet the illegal downloading of music and competition from other forms of home entertainment like computer games are severely squeezing the recording industry. Worldwide sales of albums fell by 14 per cent in 2008, following on from a 15 per cent drop the previous year. Since 2000, the total fall in sales has been a staggering 45 per cent.

Nanotechnology
The advent of digital personal stereos, such as MP3 players and iPods, means that people can now store thousands of music files downloaded from the Internet on a tiny device. The new iPod Nano launched by Apple in 2008 (left) comes in all the colours of the rainbow.

Let there be light!

Thomas Alva Edison is widely remembered as the inventor of the electric light. But in purely technical terms, at least 20 of his contemporaries could well have pipped him to the post. Little wonder there was such keen competition – the idea of the lightbulb had been around for almost a century.

US patent number 223898, filed on 4 November, 1879, credits Edison with inventing the incandescent lamp. This consisted of a very fine filament, coiled and stretched between two electrodes, enclosed within a glass bulb containing a vacuum. No-one questions the date of Edison's patent, but the rest of the story is surrounded by uncertainty. It is now widely accepted that the light bulb was the joint brainchild of Edison and Joseph Swan, who submitted the first British patent in 1880.

First flickers

The origins of the light bulb go back to 1801 and British chemist Sir Humphry Davy's discovery that an electric current could induce incandescence. Using electricity from a Voltaic pile, Davy heated a thin strip of platinum until it began to glow. The effect lasted only for a moment, as the platinum rapidly oxidised in the air, but scientists soon began to realise the advantages that electric lighting could have over naked flames from candles, gas or oil, which gave off poor light, were smelly and a fire hazard into the bargain. The trick was to get the filament to glow for longer – a problem that took 75 years to solve.

The development of the incandescent lamp stepped up a gear in 1840, when the English chemist Warren de la Rue passed an electric current through a platinum coil sealed in a vacuum tube. De la Rue realised that an evacuated tube would contain fewer oxygen molecules to react with the platinum filament, thus causing it to burn out more slowly. But a practical commercial application of this insight was still a long way off: at the time there was no efficient means of creating a vacuum and platinum was far too expensive. Even so, this did not prevent the British inventor Frederick de Moleyns from submitting the world's first patent for an incandescent lamp in 1841.

Trial and error
In Edison's original carbon-filament bulb (right), the vacuum inside the glass was so efficient the filament did not burn out, despite becoming white-hot. The four different designs for light bulbs (above) were produced by Edison between 1879 and 1883. He tested several types of filament and bulb shapes in order to find the optimal combination and ensure the longest burning time, eventually producing a bulb that could glow for more than 1,200 hours.

ELECTRICITY FOR ALL

Edison gave the first public demonstration of his carbon-filament incandescent light bulb at his Menlo Park research laboratory on 31 December, 1879. Legend has it that he confidently declared to the assembled crowd of around 3,000 expectant onlookers that 'We will make electricity so cheap that only the rich will burn candles'.

Battle of the bulbs

In 1845 the American John Wellington Starr patented an incandescent bulb using filaments made from carbon, which was far less costly. This material was used in all bulbs until the arrival of tungsten filaments. In 1893 the German-American Heinrich Göbel tried to have Edison's patent revoked on the grounds that he, Göbel, had designed the first practical bulb in 1854 with a filament made from carbonised bamboo. The judge ruled that Göbel's claim was 'extremely improbable'.

Yet the fiercest dispute was between Swan and Edison. From 1877 to 1880, while Swan was busy developing a lamp with a filament of carbonised cotton thread, Edison filed a series of patents for platinum and carbon-filament bulbs. He also purchased many other inventors' patents. Swan was less interested in commercial exploitation, but to avoid a costly court battle, the two men agreed in 1883 to found a joint company called the Edison and Swan United Electric Company ('Ediswan') to manufacture

WHITE HEAT

The incandescence of a light-bulb filament is produced by an electric current passing through a material (a conductor) and heating it. Electric irons and heaters operate on the same principle, but in the case of the light bulb the filament literally becomes white-hot (in excess of 3,000°C), which causes it to radiate light.

and market the bulb in Britain. Eventually, Edison acquired all of Swan's shares in the firm.

Competing claims for the relative longevity and brightness of bulbs continued until the invention of the tungsten filament by William D Coolidge in 1910. For the rest of the century incandescent light bulbs reigned supreme, until concerns over energy-saving saw them being phased out in favour of low-energy fluorescent bulbs in the early 2000s. These emit the same amount of light but consume a quarter of the energy and last five to six times as long.

The city that never sleeps
New York at night, seen from the top of the Empire State Building. Edison built the first electricity generating plant in the city – the Pearl Street Station – in 1882, initially supplying 110 volts DC to 85 customers in Lower Manhattan powering a total of 400 bulbs. Within two years, the facility was serving more than 500 customers and lighting more than 10,000 bulbs.

Archetype of the modern entrepreneur

Between 1869 – the date of his first invention – and his death in 1931, Edison submitted an astonishing 1,093 patents. More importantly, he was the first to forge a link between industry and the world of science and technology.

'His method [of working] was inefficient in the extreme ... at first, I was almost a sorry witness of his doings, knowing that just a little theory and calculation would have saved him 90 per cent of the labour. But he had a veritable contempt for book learning and mathematical knowledge, trusting himself entirely to his inventor's instinct and practical American sense.' This somewhat downbeat assessment of Thomas Alva Edison appeared in the *New York Times* on 19 October, 1931, the day after Edison's death. It was written by Nikola Tesla, a Croatian-born Serbian electrical engineer who had first arrived in America back in 1884 and gone to work for Edison. Tesla's obituary of his former employer was one of the few that did not lionise the 'Wizard of Menlo Park,' as the press had dubbed the great American inventor. And Tesla had good reason to be bitter: he was the uncredited co-author – perhaps even the sole author – of no fewer than 700 or so of the inventions patented in Edison's name.

Courting controversy

During his lifetime, Edison was adored and loathed in equal measure. On the one hand he was acclaimed as a genius; on the other he was a controversial figure, accused of making capital out of the inventions of others and of claiming his employees' ideas as his own. With hindsight, we can appreciate the magnitude of his achievement. He was the first person with the vision and foresight to bring science, technology and industry together and to realise that commercial imperatives were a highly effective stimulus to technical research and development, or R&D.

Entrepreneur extraordinaire
A portrait of Edison (above) painted in 1890 by Abraham Archibald Anderson. The original is in the US National Portrait Gallery in Washington DC.

Market news
Edison's version of the stock telegraph printer (left), so called because it used tickertape to display the prices of stocks and shares.

EDISON AND THE TELEGRAPH

Edison spent much of 1868–9 improving the tickertape machine, a device invented in 1867 by Edward Calahan to transmit stock price information in Morse code over telegraph lines. The Automatic Telegraph Company (ATC) paid Edison $40,000 for his machine, which sent 500 words a minute. Five years later, he devised a way of sending two messages simultaneously over one telegraph line – or four messages in each direction over the common arrangement of a pair of wires. Edison sold this 'perfected quadruplex telegraph' to Western Union for $10,000.

Edison himself once famously claimed that 'genius is 1 per cent inspiration and 99 per cent perspiration'. By this definition, there is no question that he was a genius. Entirely self-taught, he was a prolific inventor from his youth right up to his death, a polymath who epitomised the American ideal of the self-made man. He founded 14 companies – including the electricity giant, General Electric – and set up the first private research laboratory, which became the model for all subsequent R&D departments attached to commercial enterprises. He pioneered the electric light and power distribution in cities and he also made a significant contribution to the early history of the cinema.

Tough childhood

Edison's highly complex personality could be traced to his troubled childhood. The youngest of seven children born to Nancy Eliot and Samuel Edison, a Canadian exiled to the USA for anti-government activities, Thomas had an upbringing that verged on abusive. At the age of 6, he developed hearing problems as a result of scarlet fever and untreated middle-ear infections; this left him half-deaf and unable to attend school, so he was taught at home by his mother. Aged 8, he began selling newspapers and sweets on the Port Huron to Detroit railroad, a formative experience that gave him a lifelong head for business.

In mid-19th century America, the railways, with the electric telegraph running alongside to link stations, were at the cutting edge of technology. Around the age of 15, Edison saved the young son of the stationmaster at Mount Clemens, Michigan, from being hit by a train. In gratitude, the station agent trained Edison as a telegraph operator. By 1869 he was a telegrapher for the Western Union Company, wiring news for the Associated Press bureau. The telegraph would be Edison's entry-point into the world of inventing, as he began tinkering with the equipment and making improvements to it.

The Wizard of Menlo Park

Edison's first patent, lodged in 1869, was for an electric vote recorder. He then turned his attention to installing a more effective microphone in Alexander Graham Bell's brand-new telephone. With the money he earned from these early patents, Edison was able to set up his own research lab in Menlo Park, taking on assistants to help develop his multitude of ideas. In the meantime, in 1871, he married the 16-year-old Mary Stilwell, who would bear him three children.

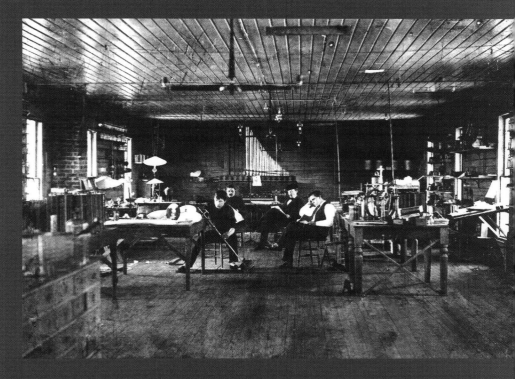

Inventors at work

Edison's own name for his Menlo Park laboratory was 'the inventions factory'. This photograph (above) shows the lab in 1880 with four of his assistants: left to right – George Hill, Charles Hughes, Samuel Mott and Francis Jehl. Edison often played the organ (seen against the back wall) for relaxation after hours of hard work.

Guiding light

The 40-metre-high Edison Memorial Tower (right) was erected in 1938 in the town of Menlo Park, which was renamed Edison in 1954. The giant lightbulb-shaped beacon burns throughout the night.

EDISON'S CARBON MICROPHONE

In 1877–8, Edison created a carbon microphone for the new telephone invented by Alexander Graham Bell. This transformed sound waves into electrical impulses and remained in use right up to the 1980s. Despite a rival claim by Emile Berliner, which resulted in a long legal battle, Edison eventually sold the rights for the microphone to Western Union for $100,000.

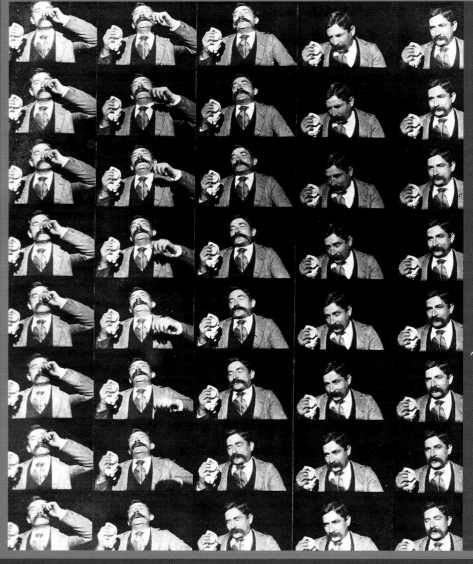

WINDOW ON THE CINEMA

In 1888 Edison first described the concept of the kinetoscope, which basically contained all the elements of the coming (more successful) cinematograph. Crucially, one thing the kinetoscope could not do was project images onto a screen. Instead, individual viewers peered through a viewfinder in the top of the kinetoscope cabinet – like this production model of 1894 (below) – to watch a short film. Most of the work on the kinetoscope was carried out by Edison's assistant William Dickson, who built various prototypes between 1889 and 1892.

Staging a sneeze
One of the first films made for viewing on a kinetoscope was this sequence, produced in 1895, featuring one of Edison's employees, Fred Ott, taking a pinch of snuff to make himself sneeze. The same year saw the opening of the first public kinetoscope parlours in New York and London.

NOT SO FAR-SIGHTED

In 1880 Edison told his associate Sam Insull 'The phonograph is not of any commercial value'. Wrong again, in 1922 he predicted that 'The radio craze will die out ...'

Edison's real rise to fame and fortune began in 1877, with his invention of the phonograph. This was a stroke of genius out of the blue. Scientists had already shown that sound vibrations could be transferred by means of a stylus onto cylinders covered in lamp-black, but nobody before Edison (and almost simultaneously the Frenchman Charles Cros) ever dreamt of playing back the recorded sound. The public were instantly captivated.

Power to the people

Next came the long-running saga of the incandescent light bulb. The technology necessary for electric lighting had been worked out for some years, but one seemingly insuperable problem was the short life of the filament. Edison took various existing models – notably Joseph Swan's – and set his team of assistants to work improving the design of the filament. On 22 October, 1879, their efforts were rewarded when a carbon-filament bulb stayed alight for 40 hours, easily beating the previous record of only 10 hours.

On 4 November that same year, Edison filed a patent application for a 'high-resistance electric lamp giving light by incandescence'. But the struggle was only just beginning:

others immediately challenged his claim. Without waiting for the outcome of the dispute, Edison forged ahead and developed electric power distribution networks to supply his bulbs. He realised that he could only corner this hotly contested market if he created lighting systems on a grand scale. This led him to design a direct current (DC) generator, which he constantly refined between 1878 and 1887. The late 1880s saw the outbreak of a 'War of the Currents' between Edison's DC system and the rival alternating current (AC) promoted by George Westinghouse and Nikola Tesla. In the long-run, AC emerged victorious, since it could carry electricity for hundreds of miles with only minimal power loss.

A PACIFIST AT WAR

Edison was asked to work as a consultant for the US Navy during the First World War. He agreed, but because of his strong belief in non-violence, he was put in charge of a team developing defensive weapons technology, notably hydrophones for submarines to detect underwater obstacles or enemy submersibles. After the war, Edison said 'I am proud of the fact that I never invented weapons to kill'.

Active to the end

After the death of his first wife in 1884, Edison married Mina Miller, a woman 20 years his junior, in 1886, and had three more children. He also continued to work. In the early 1890s he introduced the kinetoscope (see box, far left), but his device was soon made obsolete by the Lumière Brothers' cinematograph of 1895, which could project images onto a screen. His diverse projects included a magnetic ore separator and a storage battery for a planned electric car. Just before his death – at the age of 84, on 18 October, 1931 – the Lackawanna Railroad in New Jersey had inaugurated a service running trains with electric motors powered by overhead electric power lines. The entire project had been supervised by the octogenarian Edison.

Wired for sound
Edison's carbon microphone technology was for many decades the industry standard in sound recording and radio broadcasting, as in this Bell microphone (below left) used by the BBC in 1933. Edison is pictured here (below) in later life speaking into a microphone.

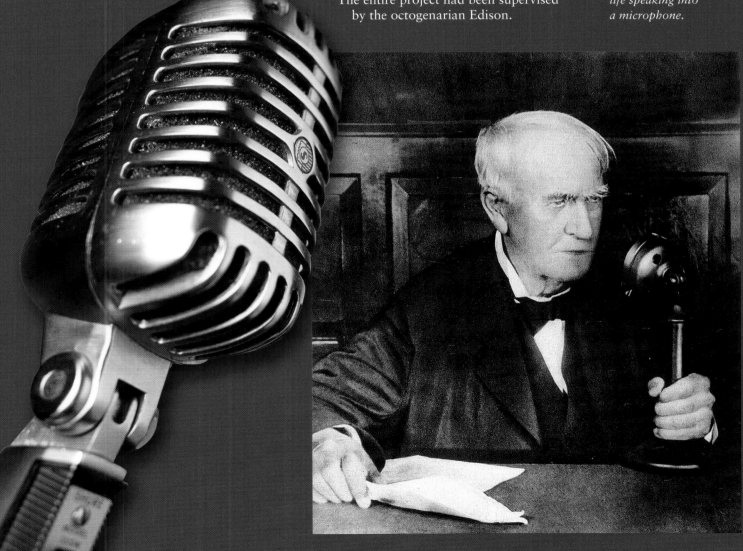

THE SAFETY BICYCLE – 1879
The world on two wheels

The 'célérifère'
A French precursor of the bicycle (above) – little more than an uncomfortable seat on wheels – created in the 1790s by Comte Mede de Sivrac.

Early attempts to produce a two-wheeled conveyance led to the 'hobby horse', the velocipede and the penny-farthing, among others. All these early machines were heavy and uncomfortable, and some were downright dangerous, but from 1860 real progress began to be made, culminating in 1879 in Henry Lawson's 'safety bicycle'.

Dandies on two wheels
A lithograph of 1819, by the sporting artist Henry Alken, shows fashionable young men of the day riding their hobby horses in London.

It is impossible to single out any one person as the inventor of the bicycle as we know it today. The machine evolved through a gradual process of adaptation and improvement involving engineers and inventors in several countries. Yet undoubtedly the single most important advance was made by the British bicycle designer Henry (also known as Harry) John Lawson. In 1879 this 27-year-old engineer from London submitted a patent for 'improvements in the construction of bicycles and other velocipedes'. Lawson's resulting 'safety bicycle', on which the rear wheel was

driven by a chain and sprocket, got its name from the fact that it was so much safer to ride than its predecessors. His design was adopted by the main manufacturers and gradually began to supplant all previous types, effectively putting an end to the era of the penny-farthing.

Beginnings of the bicycle

The story of the bicycle goes back to the year 1790 when a French noblemen, the Comte Mede de Sivrac, started taking the air in the gardens of Paris sitting astride a wooden beam mounted above two connected wheels. With no handlebars or pedals, he propelled his wheeled contraption by pushing off from the ground on either side with his feet. Sivrac called his machine the *célérifère* (from Latin, literally meaning 'quick carriage').

Some years later in Paris, on 5 April, 1818, a German engineer and forestry official named Baron Karl Friedrich Drais von Sauerbronn unveiled a machine of his own devising that built on the *célérifère*. It bore a striking resemblance to its predecessor and was pushed along with the feet in the same way, but it had a sprung seat and could be steered by means of a pivoted front wheel. The *Laufmaschine*, or 'running machine', as Drais called it, enjoyed a brief vogue among smart city dwellers in Paris, London and New York, but largely fell into disuse by around 1850 due to its weight and lack of manoeuvrability.

A revolutionary 'hobby horse'?

The next chapter in bicycle history unfolded in Scotland. In Britain the Drais-type machine became known as the 'hobby horse, and in 1839 Kirkpatrick MacMillan (1812–78), the son of a Dumfries blacksmith, built an improved version that he called a velocipede ('fast foot'). The revolutionary feature of the

---

A LIBERATING FORCE

The bicycle was a hugely liberating force for women. Not only did it allow them to take vigorous exercise, until then considered 'unladylike', but they could go out unchaperoned or even, with the arrival of the tandem, ride with a male partner. The bicycle also played a role in emancipating women's clothing, encouraging them to abandon heavy corsets and other restrictive underwear. Some young women even opted for loose trousers known as bloomers or knickerbockers, which fastened at the ankle or below the knee and became acceptable for certain sporting activities. The Bicycle Touring Club, Britain's first formal cycling association, was founded in 1878 and just two years later Mrs W D Walford became the first woman admitted.

new machine was a system of treadles and connecting rods, which the rider operated by shuffling his feet back and forth. In 1842 a Glasgow newspaper carried a report of a 'gentlemen from Dumfriesshire, astride a velocipede of ingenious design' being fined 5 shillings for knocking down a pedestrian. Popular myth has long identified MacMillan as the gentleman-cyclist, although some regard the episode as a later fabrication.

A more efficient means of propulsion

Two decades later a major step forward was taken by Pierre Michaux and his son Ernest, who ran a coachbuilding and mechanical workshop in Paris. Their interest in two-wheeled transport began when a hatter brought his hobby horse to them for repair and Ernest took it out for a test ride. He returned exhausted by the action of constantly propelling the machine along, then having to

hold his feet up off the ground between pushes. The Michauxs' first idea was to mount toe-clips on the front wheel, so at least there was somewhere to rest the feet when the machine was coasting. But then they had a better idea: they fit two pedals directly onto the spindle of the front wheel to act as cranks. They also equipped their machine with a lever brake that acted on the rim of the back wheel. Their invention was a spectacular success; from making two machines in 1861, they went on to turn out 142 in 1862 and 400 in 1865. They exhibited their 'boneshaker' at the Paris Universal

Boneshakers
Equipped with pedals and a rear brake, Ernest and Pierre Michaux's velocipedes – like the one shown above – were a major step on from the hobby horse. Even so, the iron-rimmed wooden wheels made for an uncomfortable ride over cobblestones and soon earned their machines the nickname of 'boneshakers'. By the time this picture was taken in Paris in 1910 (left), showing members of the Michaux family demonstrating their bicycles, the machines were already obsolete.

Exposition of 1867, then soon after they merged their enterprise with another firm of engineers, the Olivier Brothers, to form the *Compagnie Parisienne des Vélocipèdes* (Parisian Velocipede Company). The business made an average of 12 machines a day and exported them all round the world, as far afield as India and Australia. To promote their product, the company organised the first cycle race, which took place on 31 May, 1868, in St-Cloud Park in Paris.

Enter the high-wheeler

Thereafter front wheels became ever larger, as manufacturers tried to increase the distance covered by each turn of the pedals and thus make their machines go faster. The 1870s and 1880s were the heyday of the 'pennyfarthings', which had front wheels of more than 1.5 metres in diameter. Speed records tumbled – as did many riders: having the riding position directly above the centre of gravity was inherently dangerous.

Some inventors were prepared to buck this particular trend. As early the mid-1860s, for example, the French

Gentleman's conveyance
In this whimsical photograph (below), staged in 1956 by the British film director Ken Russell, a butler holds an umbrella over his master as the pair cycle together through Hyde Park on a boneshaker and a penny-farthing.

clockmaker André Guilmet conceived the idea of using a transmission chain, and created a velocipede driven by the rear wheel. An ingenious gearing system, whereby the front chain wheel was larger than the rear wheel hub sprocket, meant that there was no need for a huge back wheel – for each turn of the chain wheel, the rear wheel revolved twice. In 1869 Guilmet joined forces with the manufacturer Eugène Meyer to exploit his invention. Sadly, Guilmet was killed the following year during the Franco-Prussian War and their venture never got beyond the prototype phase.

'TAKING A HEADER'

The rise of the penny-farthing – nicknamed in the USA 'the horse that never says neigh' – began in 1871, when Coventry-based inventor James Starley developed and marketed the all-steel 'Ariel'. Two years later the celebrated cyclist James Moore used an Ariel to set a speed record of just over 14mph (23km/h). For the nervous, tricycle versions were also available. High-wheelers remained popular for almost 20 years and were even used for a round-the-world trip by the American Thomas Stevens between 1884 and 1886. The main problem with them was that if the front wheel hit a rut, or if an emergency stop was required, the entire bicycle rotated around the front axle and pitched the rider forward, popularly known as 'taking a header'.

the hub at an angle; this helped to ease the stress on individual spokes and made the wheels far stronger than on earlier models. By the late 1870s, bicycle frames were being made from hollow-section steel tubing. And in 1888 the Scottish veterinary surgeon John Boyd Dunlop invented the pneumatic rubber tyre, which made the ride far smoother for cyclists. He is said to have been inspired by watching his son suffer a bumpy ride and to have fashioned his first tyre from a garden hose

Dunlop's original tyres were not very practical – in the event of a puncture, the whole tyre had to be changed, which was quite a long and tricky operation. A solution to this

Rise of the safety bicycle

In 1879 Henry Lawson unveiled his first chain-driven velocipede, which he named the 'Crocodile'. Presently, he teamed up with the manufacturer John K Starley – whose uncle, James, had invented the high-wheeler – and launched the 'Rover Safety Bicycle' in 1885. The firm's next innovation, the following year, was a model with handlebars directly linked to the front forks. Rover also fitted their bicycles with ball bearings, which greatly reduced friction and wear in both the wheel hubs and the bottom pedal bracket.

In time, the bicycle began to take on its familiar modern appearance: two wheels of equal diameter, with the rider seated increasingly squarely and safely behind the centre of gravity. Gone were the days of acrobatics by pennyfarthing riders. Now, all manufacturers began to turn their production over to the ever more popular safety bicycle.

Rapid development

Technological innovations for the bicycle came thick and fast in the final decades of the 19th century. In 1874 James Starley introduced alternating tensioned spokes that connected to

Chain-driven
A bicycle of 1869 built by Guilmet and Meyer (above). This was the first machine to be equipped with chain transmission.

A spin in the country
A poster from 1900 promotes the Rover Safety Bicycle by appealing to the Victorian middle classes, who took to cycling as a weekend leisure activity. J K (John Kemp) Starley was the nephew of James, creator of the 'Ariel'.

BALL BEARINGS

There are competing claims over who invented the ball bearing. Philip Vaughan, a Welsh ironmaster, is reputed to have submitted the first known patent for bearings, fitted around a carriage axle, in Carmarthen in 1794. French historians cite Charles Tihay, an abbot from Grandvillers in the Vosges, as having invented ball bearings for the chimes in his church clock in the 1850s. Where bicycles are concerned, the first patent for ball bearings was awarded on 3 August, 1869, to Jules Pierre Suriray, a cycle mechanic from Paris. His bearings were fitted to a machine ridden by James Moore, who won the world's first bicycle road race from Paris to Rouen in November that year. Before long, ball bearings were being used in the cranks, pedals and headsets (the joint between the front forks and the frame) of all bicycles.

THE PARIS TO ROUEN RACE

The world's first long-distance cycle race took place in 1869 between Paris and Rouen in Normandy. It was jointly organised by the magazine *Le Vélocipède Illustré* and René Olivier of the Parisian Velocipede Company, with the aim of demonstrating that 'the bicycle can cover a considerable distance with far less effort than would be exerted by walking it'. On 7 November, cheered on by a huge crowd, 203 riders set off from the Arc de Triomphe to cover 123km (76 mile) route. The race leaders were expected to arrive in Rouen around midnight, but to everyone's astonishment the English cyclist James Moore bowled into the city at 6.10pm, having completed the race at an average speed of 11.5km/h (7mph). Only 34 of the original field made it to Rouen within the deadline of 24 hours. The historic race is still marked by an anniversary run to this day.

Gruelling race *Riders on the first Tour de France set off from Montgeron, on the outskirts of Paris, on 1 July, 1903. The winner, Maurice Garin, covered the 2,428km at an average speed of 25.47km/h. In 2009 the course covered 3,459.5km and the winner, the Spaniard Alberto Contador, averaged 40km/h.*

Ready, steady, go! *Leon Errol (centre), an Australian-American comedian, leads a group of fashion models on bicycles at a promotional event in Madison Square Gardens, New York, in 1925.*

Michelin Man
The rotund trademark tyre figure, known in his native France as 'Bibendum', is pictured here on a 1910 advertisement for bicycle tyres. In 1891 a bike fitted with Michelin inner-tube tyres won the inaugural Paris-Brest-Paris race.

problem emerged in 1891 when the French industrialist Édouard Michelin devised the inner tube, which was a great success both on bicycles and motor-cars. Puncture-repair patches made their first appearance in 1903.

Freewheel hub mechanisms were first fitted to bicycles in 1897; these prevented the pedal crank from spinning round of its own accord and also meant that the back wheel could only be pedalled in a forward direction. Meanwhile, rod-operated brakes using hard rubber blocks to grip the wheel rims became widespread. The final major innovation was the derailleur, a hub-mounted gearing system that first came on the market in 1907. Four years later, a

participant in the Tour de France used it for the first time. The derailleur enabled cyclists to pedal faster or slower, with the chain switching between sprockets mounted both on the chain wheel and the rear hub. The innovation did not meet with universal approval, as some cyclists felt that it detracted from the physical rigour of the sport. As a result, Henri Desgrange, organiser of the Tour de France, banned its use. It was 1937 before derailleur gears were reinstated in competition races.

Bicycles conquer the world

Later improvements to the bicycle have mainly focused on reducing its weight – particularly

Cutting edge *British cyclist Chris Boardman (right) setting the world 1-hour cycling speed record of 52.270 km/h on 23 July, 1993, in Bordeaux, France.*

through the use of new materials such as titanium and carbon fibre – and improving its aerodynamic profile, which led to the invention of the solid or 'lenticular' wheel. Cycling on flat terrain, behind a car-mounted screen as a shield from headwinds, cyclists have achieved speeds well in excess of 200km/h; the current record, set in 1995 by Fred Rompelberg of the Netherlands, stands at 268.831km/h (166.944mph). Bike suspension has also improved in leaps and bounds, absorbing shocks from uneven road surfaces without slowing the rider down.

There are now estimated to be almost 2 billion bicycles – town bikes, racing bikes, mountain bikes, hybrids – in use, making it the most popular mode of transport on the planet. The bike once facilitated industrialisation and continues to offer workers a cheap way to get to and from the workplace, while also offering the benefit of exercise. For obvious reasons, the bicycle is most popular in flat regions, such as the Netherlands and East Anglia, but with the increasing problem of global warming caused by carbon emissions, the rise of the bicycle looks set to continue.

Land of bicycles
In recent years the ubiquitous presence of the bicycle in communist China has declined in the face of growing car ownership. Even so, there are still an estimated 500 million bicycles in the People's Republic of China.

Saccharine
1879

Sugaring the pill
Another use for sweeteners such as saccharine is to mask the bitter taste of certain medications administered orally in the form of tablets (above). Natural sweeteners include honey, maple syrup and stevia, a plant eaten by the Guaraní Indians of Paraguay and Argentina.

In 1879, in his lab at Johns Hopkins University in Baltimore, USA, the chemist Ira Remsen was busy conducting a series of experiments on coal-tar derivatives. He consulted regularly with his assistant Constantin Fahlberg, who had created a compound of toluene and ortho-toluene sulphonamide, which he discovered tasted extremely sweet. The two scientists published their findings jointly in February 1880. Fahlberg quickly realised that his product – which he christened 'saccharine' (from the Latin *saccharum*, meaning 'sugar') – could be used as a sugar substitute. Four years later, after running toxicity tests, he filed a patent before embarking on saccharine production on an industrial scale. A furious row then erupted between him and Remsen, who accused his former colleague of having appropriated his discovery.

Sugar without calories

Saccharine, the world's first artificial sweetener, was an instant hit. It had four to five times the sweetness of sugar, but none of the nutritional value – in other words, it had zero calories and was not absorbed by the body. Until 1938 it could only be obtained on prescription in the USA, but during the Second World War, with sugar rationed, saccharine came into its own as a consumer product. Since the late 19th century, chemists have discovered a number of

SWEETER BY FAR

There are two types of sweetener. Strong sweeteners, such as aspartame or saccharine, can have up to several thousand times the sweetening power of sugar, while having a calorific count of zero. The sweetness of sugar substitutes, such as isomalt or sugar alcohols, is roughly the same as sugar and they do contain some calories. Sugar alcohols are easier to use in cooking, but in high doses have a laxative effect. The use of any sweetener in place of sugar will help to prevent tooth decay and reduce calorie intake. On the debit side, they sustain the cravings people have for sweet foods and can disrupt eating habits.

other artificial sweeteners, including dulcine (1884), cyclamate (1937), isomalt (1957) and aspartame (1965). Fifteen such compounds are now commonly used in the manufacture of sweets, jams and preserves, fizzy drinks and other reduced-sugar products. Some later studies have suggested a possible link between saccharine and certain types of cancer, but its popularity has continued among slimmers and diabetics. Although it can impart a bitter aftertaste if taken in high doses, saccharine remains a blue-chip product with an annual market estimated at 30,000–40,000 tonnes.

The cash register 1879

Behind his bar in Dayton, Ohio, saloon keeper James Ritty totted up his takings, his forehead lined with anxiety. His business was far from being a surefire money-spinner. How could he be sure some dishonest barman was not skimming his profits? The answer to his worries came on a trip to Europe. Staving off boredom on the long transatlantic crossing, he became intrigued by a mechanism that counted how many times the ship's propeller went round. Ritty surmised that the same principle could be applied to a machine for recording cash transactions.

Technical success, commercial failure

On his return to America, Ritty and his mechanic brother set about creating such a device, which they christened 'Ritty's Incorruptible Cashier'. It was fitted with revolving wheels that totalled up the shop's daily receipts on a dial with hands, like a clockface. They patented it in 1879. Later refinements included a display to show the customer what they owed. Cash registers quickly caught on with storekeepers, but the company created by Ritty was not a success. In 1884 he sold it to another businessman, John H Patterson, who renamed it the National Cash Register Company.

Ringing tills
The advent of the cash register marked the beginning of more rigorous accounting practices. Soon every transaction would generate a receipt and other financial records.

Changeover period
During the changeover to the Euro in 2001, some tills in EU countries were fitted with double cash drawers so the new currency could be kept separate from the old national currency it was replacing.

WHO INVENTED THE TILL?

James Ritty was not the only person interested in developing a cash register. In 1883 a Parisian inventor by the name of Henry Pottin developed a keyboard-operated machine for recording cash transactions at bank counters. Five years later William Burroughs, a customs official from Rochester in New York patented an adding machine. He went on to found a highly successful business automation company that became the Burroughs Corporation.

By the 1900s tills had been fitted with cash drawers, which rang when opened; some even had multiple drawers with different chimes. They had a mechanism that printed out receipts for customers as well as tallies of the day's takings, with automatic date stamps to prevent fraud. In the 1950s electric servo motors began to replace mechanical levers for opening and closing tills. The late 20th century brought electronic cash registers and automatic barcode scanning. Today, state-of-the-art cash register technology allows store managers to tell almost at a glance which product lines are selling well, enabling them to assess stock levels and reorder efficiently.

Portrait of a 19th-century city

Late 19th-century London was the biggest city in the world and a teeming hive of activity. Its heavy industry worked day and night, while at its heart lay a dynamic centre of business and commerce. London's Docks, the largest in the world, were a bustling entrepôt for international trade. Foreign visitors to the 1851 Great Exhibition must have been by turns fascinated and appalled at the majesty and squalor on display in the capital of the British Empire.

Industrial powerhouse

Battersea Power Station in the 1950s (below right). Industry in London had begun to crowd around the banks of the Thames, an ideal artery for transporting raw materials, from c1810. As waste spewed into the water and smoke into the air, the river and the city grew ever more polluted.

By 1880 London had 15 mainline stations serving all the major cities around Britain. Ships flying the flags of countries all round the globe accounted for more than 75,000 sailings annually in and out of London Docks. The vast complex of wharves in the city's East End employed around 100,000 dockers either permanent or day labourers. This army of dockers worked on quaysides packed with every conceivable kind of ship – clippers, brigs, schooners, lighters and steamers. As far as the eye could see, warehouses were piled high with all manner of goods, from wheat, tea, wool and furs to metals and elephant tusks, either just arrived at the port from far-flung parts of the empire or awaiting export.

Warehouse of the world

Virtually every branch of industry was active in London except for iron and steelmaking. Far from the smart residential districts of the West End, with their elegant townhouses and parks, the poor eastern and southeastern quarters were home to London's factories. Day and night, their chimneys belched smoke into a sky already darkened by the fog to which the low-lying London basin was prone. In the winter of 1879–80, for example, London lay under a permanent shroud of fog from November to February. Every year, industry and domestic fires in the capital consumed some 18 million tons of coal. The population of Greater London exceeded 4.75 million people at a time when Paris numbered 2.3 million and Berlin 1.1 million. Although the population of the actual City of London shrank to just 50,000, the rest of London kept expanding in all directions.

Great Britain enjoyed unrivalled power in the final decades of the 19th century. Despite

Global goods

An engraving made in 1877 by William Bazett Murray shows Chinese coolies unloading tea crates at London Docks.

LONDON'S ATMOSPHERIC SMOG

The 'smog' (a contraction of 'smoke' and 'fog') that characterised London in the 19th century and the first half of the 20th could be deadly, particularly in winter when it caused respiratory illnesses. But many artists were inspired by its atmospheric effects. The impressionist painter Claude Monet visited the city several times, completing a celebrated series of studies of Westminster viewed from the south side of the Thames. Recently, researchers from Birmingham University have used the paintings of Monet and his contemporaries to try to identify what airborne particulates were present in London's notorious 'pea-soupers'. One of the city's worst smogs occurred in 1880; it lasted three days and killed more than 2,000 people. Worst hit of all was the low-lying East End which had the highest concentration of factories.

Deadly beauty
The chromatic richness of London's smog was captured by Monet in his 1904 work Houses of Parliament, London, Sun Breaking through the Fog *(above right). The painting is in the Musée d'Orsay, Paris.*

Oiling the wheels
Lloyd's of London, the insurance syndicate created in the late 17th century, was given a sound legal framework by Act of Parliament in 1871. This engraving from an Illustrated London News *of that year shows some of the Lloyd's investors (far right).*

having just over 2 per cent of the world's total population, it produced no less than half of the world's coal and steel output, owned 34 per cent of all merchant shipping and was responsible for 25 per cent of all exports worldwide. At the heart of the Empire sat Queen Victoria, who had been on the throne since 1837. Since her accession, the official royal residence in London had been Buckingham Palace which boasted 690 rooms. Victoria's latest grand title, Empress of India, was added by Prime Minister Disraeli in 1876. She ruled over an empire on which 'the sun never set', embracing one-fifth of the habitable globe and almost one-quarter of all its inhabitants – some 400 million people.

London's pulsating heart

One of the touchstones of British supremacy was the City, London's financial centre, where even the slightest tremor on the markets could send shockwaves round the world. Every working day, almost 800,000 pedestrians and 80,000 horse-drawn carriages went to work in the City. The nerve centres were the Bank of England – the so-called 'Old Lady of Threadneedle Street', which became a model for other central banks worldwide – the Stock Exchange, the Royal Exchange and Lloyd's

insurance underwriters. A host of public and private financial institutions grew up around these, all competing in the cut-throat market. The 'square mile' of EC1 also played host to the law courts, public libraries and the diamond trade. And the great organs of the British press like the *Daily Telegraph* and *The Times* had their offices on Fleet Street.

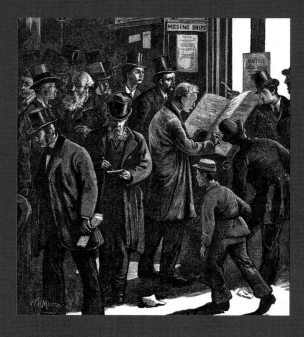

was equipped with gas street lighting from the 1840s onwards. In the 1860s the capital tackled its sewage problems through the installation of an extensive sewer drainage system masterminded by the engineer Joseph Bazalgette. It was not before time: by 1857 some 250 tons of raw sewage – plus the effluent from factories, abattoirs, tanneries – ended up in the Thames every year. Outbreaks of cholera had been common since the 1840s. In the summer of 1858 the stench from the river became known as the 'Great Stink'. It was so unbearable that river excursions were cancelled and the curtains in the Houses of Parliament were soaked in chloride of lime in an attempt to mask the appalling miasma.

Congested city
A painting by Harley Crossley, Royal London Exchange, *shows the bustling City traffic in the early 1900s.*

Spearheading progress

Before long the main arteries of the expanding capital became so chronically choked with the daily influx of hackney cabs and omnibuses that traffic could scarcely move. In response, London's planners set about taking traffic underground. On 10 January, 1863, London inaugurated its first tube service – the first in the world – with the opening of the steam-powered Metropolitan line from Paddington to Farringdon Street. Even on its first day, the service carried 30,000 passengers. The first electrified line, the City and South London Railway, came into service in 1890. London

A DANGEROUS PLACE?

In the late 1880s the East End was terrorised by the world's first documented serial killer. 'Jack the Ripper' murdered at least five prostitutes in the poor working-class Whitechapel district. But for all the notoriety of the case, London was one of the safest cities in Europe. The murder rate for the city in the 1880s was 0.9 homicides per 100,000 inhabitants – around half that of Paris.

Gateway to London *Built in 1894, Tower Bridge (below) was at the cutting edge of bridge technology in its day. The Gothic twin towers housed powerful steam engines to raise the bascule mechanism supporting the roadway. This allowed large ships to pass through into the mooring area upstream in the 'Pool of London'.*

High society

The 'London season' began every year in April, as Britain's richest and most influential people left their country seats and came up to town. They would remain in their homes in the wealthy districts of Mayfair and around Park Lane (north of Piccadilly, to the east of Hyde Park) until the end of August.

The season offered a host of delights – a dizzying round of dinner engagements and balls, viewings of the latest paintings at the Royal Academy's summer show, attending the opera at Covent Garden, cycling excursions, cricket matches, regattas on the Thames, not to mention Derby Day at Epsom. (The inordinate fondness for horse racing typical not just of Londoners but of the British as a whole caused one irreverent wag to remark that 'after Her Most Gracious Majesty Queen Victoria, the most admired, revered and famous personage in Great Britain is the horse'.) At the race course fashionable London society rubbed shoulders with the lower classes. Other venues where such a mingling took place included the Egyptian Hall (a venue in Piccadilly famous for magic shows),

Madame Tussaud's waxworks and chamber of horrors, and the 50 or so theatres; melodramas were the popular genre of the day.

Another favourite haunt was Harrods department store in Knightsbridge, whose motto was *Omnia Omnibus Ubique* ('All Things for all People, Everywhere'). This thriving enterprise had begun in 1849, when the grocer Charles Harrod decided to relocate his business from the East End to Hyde Park in order to exploit trade at the forthcoming Great Exhibition in Hyde Park. His son transformed the enterprise from a small family stall to a business employing 100 people. Large display windows allowed shoppers to view goods day or night, while all items in the store were sold at a fixed price. In 1898 Harrods installed the first escalator in England; as nervous customers stepped off the moving staircase, they were offered a glass of brandy to help revive them.

London was also a honeypot for writers. Charles Dickens lived there until 1860, when he moved out to Gadshill in Kent. From 1876 to 1886 the American novelist Henry James lived at number 3 Bolton Street in Piccadilly. In 1884 the Irish dramatist, poet and novelist Oscar Wilde took up residence at 34 Tite Street in the fashionable district of Chelsea; he was regularly to be seen holding court at the Café Royal in Regent Street.

British icon
The first public telephones appeared in Victorian London, but the famous red phone boxes were only introduced in 1926.

Jolly boating weather
After the Thames was cleansed of sewage, it became fashionable to take sightseeing boat trips around the Pool of London, like this boating party captured by James Tissot in his 1876 painting, The Thames *(top).*

143

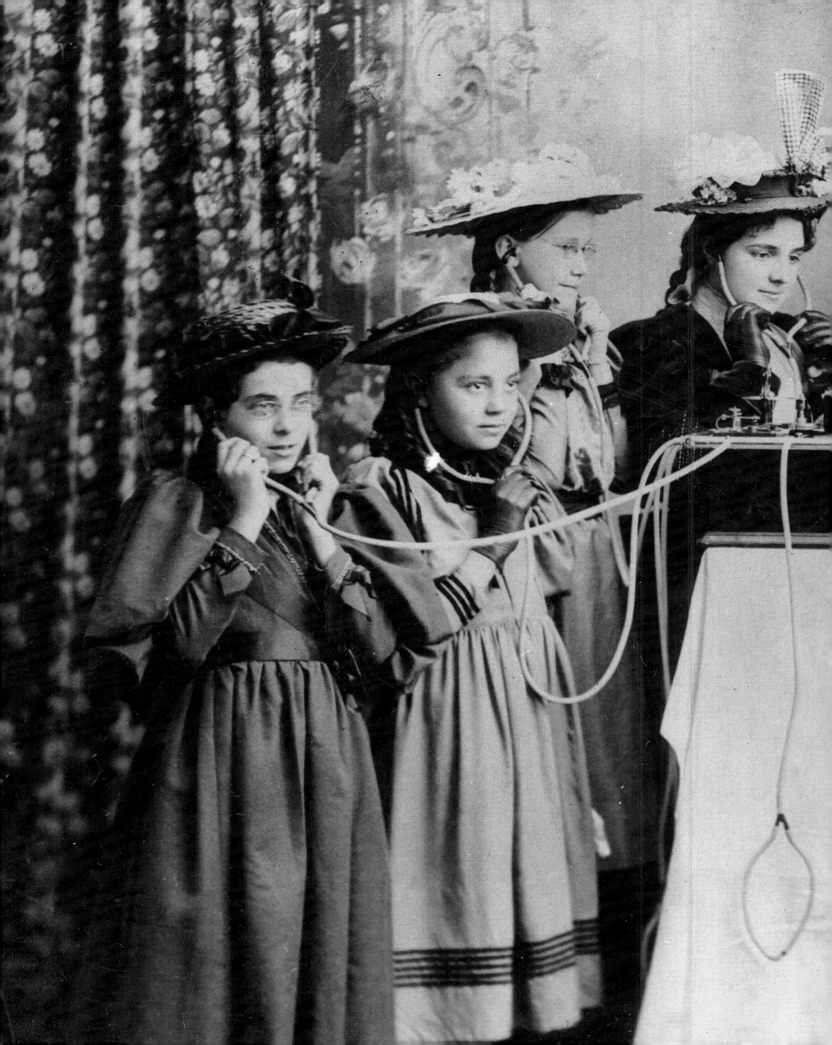

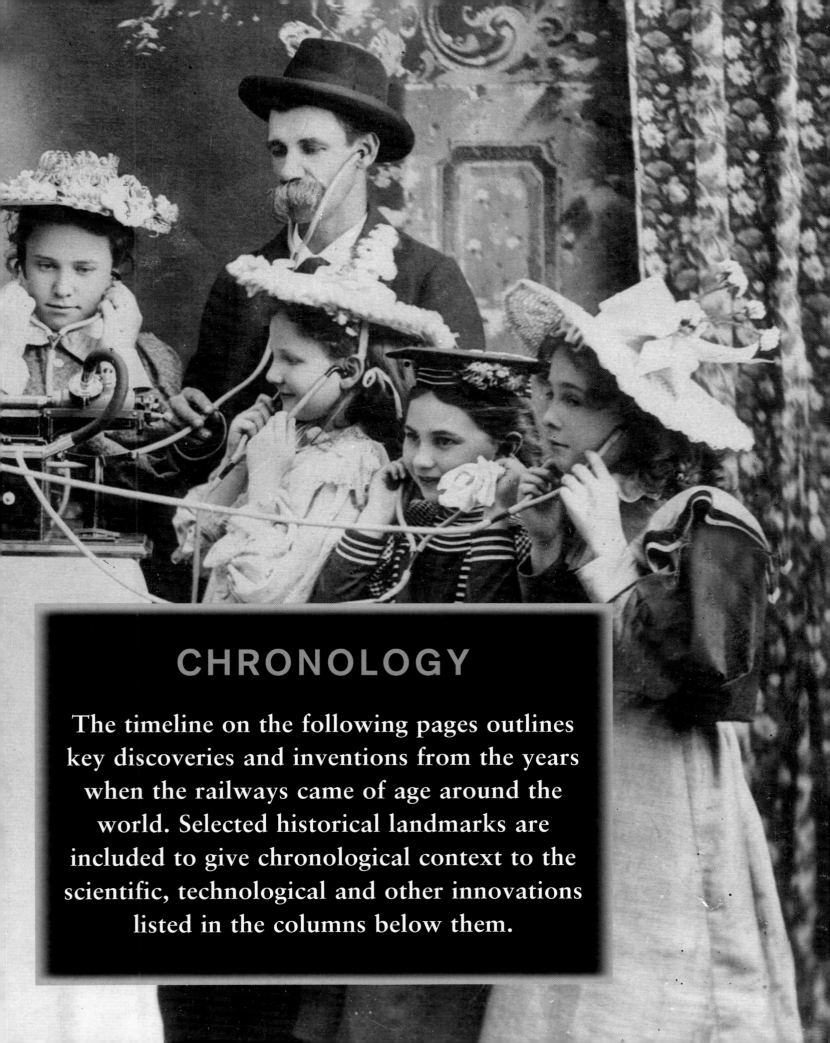

CHRONOLOGY

The timeline on the following pages outlines key discoveries and inventions from the years when the railways came of age around the world. Selected historical landmarks are included to give chronological context to the scientific, technological and other innovations listed in the columns below them.

1845

EVENTS

- Publication of the Communist Party Manifesto by Karl Marx and Friedrich Engels (1846)
- The Mexican-American War ends badly for Mexico (1848)
- Europe experiences a 'Year of Revolutions' (1848)
- The California Gold Rush gets underway (1848)

INVENTIONS

- Austrian chemist Anton von Schrötter discovers a process for preparing red phosphorus, which led eventually to the invention of the safety match

- Richard Hoe invents a rotary press capable of printing 18,000 double-sided sheets per hour

- First sighting of the planet Neptune by astronomers at the Berlin Observatory

- Ascanio Sobrero in Italy and Christian Friedrich Schönbein in Germany separately discover nitroglycerin (nitrocellulose) by soaking cotton in nitric acid

- US surgeon William Morton patents the use of ether as an anaesthetic during operations

- William Thomson (later Lord Kelvin) devises a scale of absolute temperature, in which zero is set at −273.15°C

- Hippolyte Fizeau measures the speed of light

◀ A sample of steel produced by the Bessemer process

1850

EVENTS

- Persecution of the Bah'ai faith in Persia (1850)
- Napoleon III is crowned emperor of France and the Second Empire is established (1852)

INVENTIONS

- The successful laying of an underwater cable completes the first international telegraph link between London and Paris

- In Paris, French physicist Léon Foucault completes his famous experiments on the pendulum, and uses a gyroscope to demonstrate the rotation of the Earth; he also undertakes pioneering work in optics, astronomy and electromagnetism

- The Great Exhibition is staged in London's Hyde Park

- Johan Edvard Lundstrom invents the safety match

▲ A Neanderthal skull unearthed in 1856

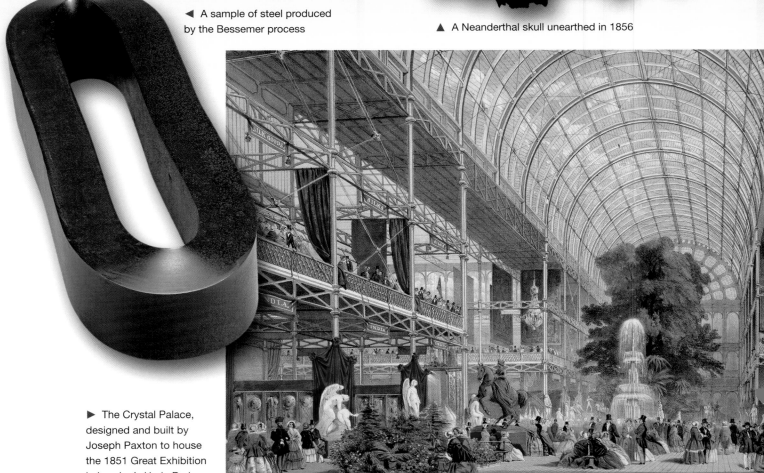

▶ The Crystal Palace, designed and built by Joseph Paxton to house the 1851 Great Exhibition in London's Hyde Park

1853

- US warships under Commodore Matthew Perry force Japan to open its ports to Western trade (1853)
- Outbreak of the Crimean War (1854)

- French physician Charles Gabriel Pravaz and Scottish doctor Alexander Wood independently invent the hypodermic syringe

- Heinrich Göbel, a German émigré to New York, constructs a prototype of the incandescent electric lamp

- English doctor John Snow identifies unclean, infected water as the source of cholera and takes steps to combat the spread of the disease in London

1855

- Russia and Japan sign a treaty on the sovereignty of Sakhalin and the Kuril Islands (1855)
- Alexander II becomes Tsar of Russia (1855)
- Beginning of the Indian Mutiny against British rule (1857)

- Henry Bessemer invents a process for converting iron to steel on an industrial scale

- William Henry Perkin manufactures the world's first artificial dye, mauveine

- Prehistoric fossilised human remains are discovered in the Neander valley in Germany

- Gail Borden patents a method for making condensed milk using heat and a vacuum pan

- Joseph Gayetty introduces toilet paper

▶ Original phials of mauveine dye from the laboratory of its inventor, William Henry Perkin

▼ An early advertisement for condensed milk

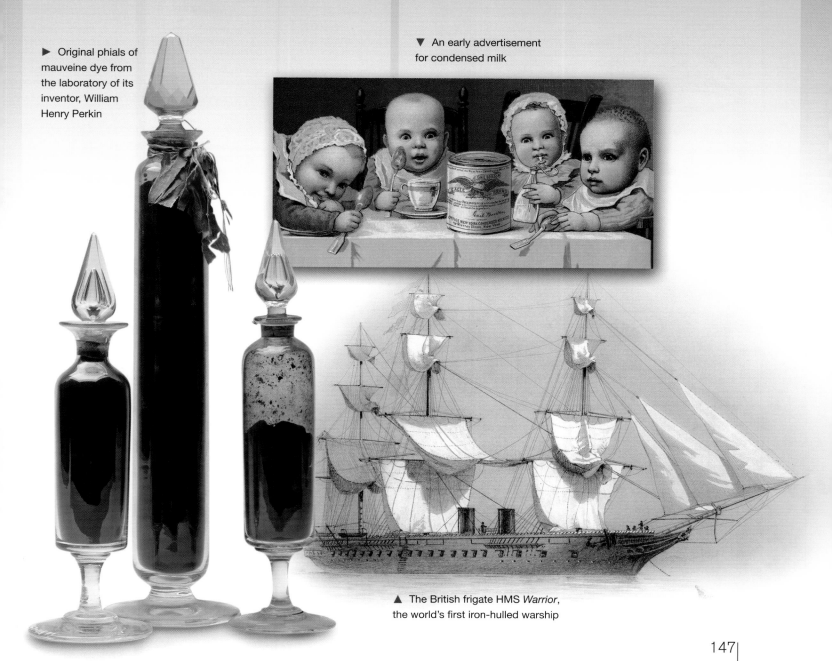

▲ The British frigate HMS *Warrior*, the world's first iron-hulled warship

147

1858

EVENTS

• The British government abolishes the East India Company and takes over the governance of India (1858)
• French forces occupy Saigon in their conquest of Cochin China (1859)
• Piedmont declares war on Austria, an important step towards Italian unification (1859)

INVENTIONS

• Edwin Drake drills the world's first commercial oil well in Pennsylvania

• The English naturalist Charles Darwin publishes *On the Origin of Species by Means of Natural Selection,* setting out his theory of evolution which was later universally accepted by science

• The French naval architect Henri Dupuy de Lôme builds the first ironclad battleship

• Étienne Lenoir pioneers the development of the internal combustion engine

1860

EVENTS

• The reforms of Tsar Alexander II lead to the abolition of serfdom in Russia (1861)
• The American Civil War begins (1861)
• Wilhelm I is crowned King of Prussia (1861)
• Victor Emmanuel II is crowned as the first ruler of the Kingdom of Italy (1861)

INVENTIONS

• Linus Yale develops the modern cylinder lock, operated by a flat, ridged key

• Germain Sommeiller devises and constructs a pneumatic drill for cutting rock, first used in the construction of the Mont Cenis tunnel

• Richard J Gatling patents the machine gun

▼ Edwin Drake (below, centre) photographed in front of his oil well, the first in the USA, near Titusville, Pennsylvania

▲ Different beak shapes of Galápagos finches, as sketched by Charles Darwin

▲ A gas engine following the Langen-Otto design built in Manchester c1876

1863

- Cambodia becomes a French protectorate (1863)
- Abraham Lincoln prolaims the emancipation of slaves in the USA (1863)
- The International Workingmen's Association, or First International, is founded and holds its first meeting in London (1864)
- Signing of the First Geneva Convention (1864)

- George Fellows Harrington invents the dentist's drill

- The rules of association football are laid down at a meeting of London club representatives

- From his work on wine fermentation, Louis Pasteur devises pasteurisation, a process for preserving foodstuffs that will revolutionise the food industry

- The world's first underground railway line is opened in London

- James Clerk Maxwell demonstrates the existence of electromagnetic and radio waves

1865

- Assassination of US President Abraham Lincoln (1865)
- The Second Reform Act introduces almost universal male suffrage in Britain (1867)
- Beginning of the Meiji Restoration period in Japan (1867)
- Formation of the Dual Monarchy of Austria-Hungary (1867)

- British surgeon Joseph Lister pioneers the use of antiseptics

- Georges Leclanché builds the Leclanché cell, an early form of battery that supplanted the Voltaic pile

- The first barbed wire is used in fences in the United States

◄ An antiseptic spray, part of the surgical equipment used by Joseph Lister

▼ A 19th-century football, with stitched leather panels

► The scene at King's Cross in 1861 as the Metropolitan Line was constructed by the 'cut-and-cover' method: a trench was dug along the length of the Euston Road, the underground railway tunnel was formed with bricks, then the road was relaid over the top

1868

1870

EVENTS

- First Vatican Council convoked by Pope Pius IX (1868)
- Shogun power is ended in Japan (1868)
- Wyoming is the first American state to give women the vote (1869)

- Outbreak of the Franco-Prussian (1870) leads to a heavy defeat for France and the loss of Alsace-Lorraine (1871)
- Founding of the French Third Republic (1870) and the Paris Commune (1871)
- German Second Empire proclaimed by Kaiser Wilhelm I (1871)
- Trade unions are granted legal recognition in Britain (1871)

INVENTIONS

- Hippolyte Mège-Mouriès develops margarine
- The Suez Canal, the brainchild of French engineer Ferdinand de Lesseps, is opened to shipping
- American Ives McGaffey patents the first vacuum cleaner

- The electric dynamo, a device the produces direct current, is invented by Belgian Zénobe Gramme
- German archaeologist Heinrich Schliemann identifies the site of Troy in Turkey
- David Boyle patents a refrigeration machine that works by ammonia compression

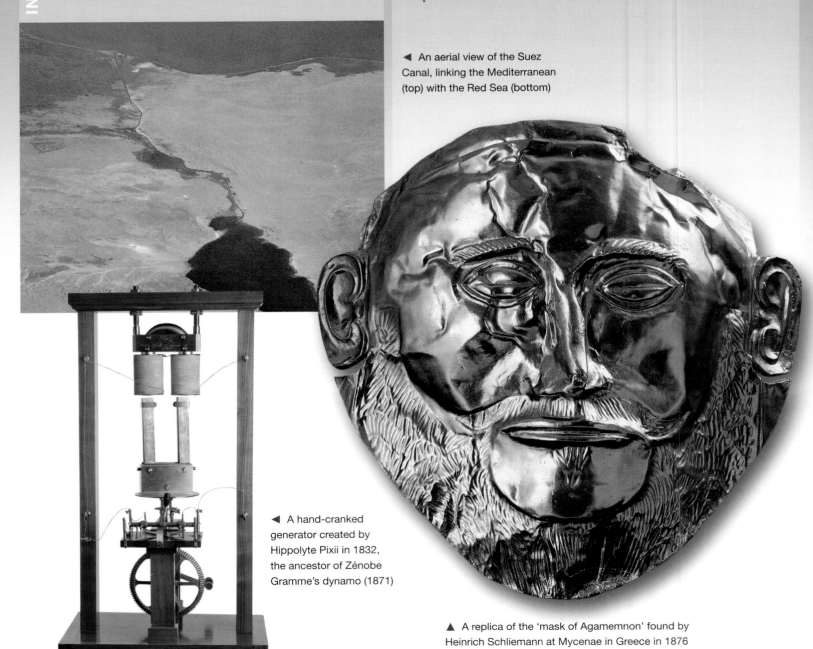

◄ An aerial view of the Suez Canal, linking the Mediterranean (top) with the Red Sea (bottom)

◄ A hand-cranked generator created by Hippolyte Pixii in 1832, the ancestor of Zénobe Gramme's dynamo (1871)

▲ A replica of the 'mask of Agamemnon' found by Heinrich Schliemann at Mycenae in Greece in 1876

1873

- Proclamation of the First Spanish Republic (1873) before Spain's Bourbon monarchy is restored (1874)
- Great Britain annexes the Fiji Islands (1874)

- The American Remington Company patents the typewriter

- Levi Strauss & Co begin marketing denim jeans as workwear for cowboys and miners in California

▶ Levi's original 501 jeans were first produced in 1873

1875

- Abdülhamid II ascends the Ottoman throne (1876)
- Native Indian tribes of the North American plains revolt against encroachment on their land by gold prospectors (1876)
- Custer's last stand (1876)
- Russo-Turkish War (1877)

- Oskar Hertwig observes the fertilisation of a cell, confirming the joint role of the sperm and the egg in reproduction

- Alexander Graham Bell lodges a patent for the telephone; units of sound measurement (bels, decibels) are named in his honour

- The phonograph is invented in France by Charles Cros and in the USA by Thomas Alva Edison, a prolific and diverse inventor equally renowned for forging a close link between technology and industry

▼ Prototype of Bell's first telephone of 1876

◀ A singer gives her performance with an 'orchestra' made up entirely of gramophones, recorded in a painting after an engraving by Friedrich Gehrke

151

1878

EVENTS

- Outbreak of the Second Anglo-Afghan War (1878)
- The Congress of Berlin attempts to resolve the Balkan crisis (1878)
- Great Britain colonises Nigeria (1879)

INVENTIONS

- Paris stages the International Exposition of 1878

- The incandescent electric light is patented by Thomas Alva Edison

- The introduction of the safety bicycle by Henry John Lawson marks the beginning of the modern era of cycling for sport and recreation

- Ira Remsen and Constantin Fahlberg create saccharine, the world's first artificial sweetener

- James Ritty introduces the cash register

1880

EVENTS

- Tsar Alexander III ascends the Russian throne (1881)
- Formation of the Triple Alliance mutual defence pact between Germany, Austria-Hungary and Italy (1882)
- Great Britain occupies Egypt (1882)

INVENTIONS

- The world's first electric power station comes on line in London, generating electricity for lighting

- Louis Pasteur develops the first artificially produced vaccine, against anthrax

- In an attempt to improve industrial efficiency, Frederick Winslow Taylor introduces his 'scientific management' techniques, including time-and-motion studies

- In Berlin, Werner von Siemens demonstrates the *Elektromote*, the forerunner of the trolleybus

- French physiologist Étienne-Jules Marey invents a camera that can take several pictures of the same scene in a short space of time – a precursor of the modern movie camera – that enables scientists to study the movement of humans and animals closely for the first time

▲ Visitors riding the 'moving pavement' at the 1900 Universal Exposition held in Paris

▶ The incandescent electric lamp, an invention created separately in 1880 by Thomas Edison and Joseph Swan

▼ A boneshaker (on the left) and penny-farthing being ridden in Hyde Park

1883

• Eruption of Krakatoa, a volcano lying between Java and Sumatra, kills 36,000 people (1883)
• The Congress of Berlin decides on European 'spheres of influence' in Africa (1884)
• Togo and Cameroon are made German protectorates (1884)

• Lewis Edson Waterman patents the 'stylograph', prototype of the modern fountain pen

• Serbian-American inventor Nikola Tesla invents the electric alternator, a generator that produces alternating current (AC)

• By adding boric acid to silicon dioxide, Carl Zeiss develops a glass resistant to heat, shock and chemical damage

• Ottmar Mergenthaler invents the Linotype typesetting machine, greatly reducing the time and effort involved in preparing text for printing

► Saccharine – the world's first artificial sweetener, invented in 1879 – in tablet form

▼ Edison's kinetoscope, created in 1888

1885

• The Dawes Act confines Native North Americans to reservations (1887)
• The French create the Indochinese Union from Vietnam, Cambodia and Laos (1887)
• The attempt by Ferdinand de Lesseps to dig the Panama Canal ends in failure and financial scandal (1889)

• The first transcontinental rail link in Canada, the Canadian Pacific Railway, is completed

• German engineer Wilhelm Maybach develops the first motorcycle for the Daimler company

• John Styth Pemberton devises the recipe for Coca-Cola

• Air-filled (pneumatic) rubber tyres are introduced by John Boyd Dunlop

• Hungarian inventor David Gestetner constructs the 'stencil duplicator', distant ancestor of the photocopier

• The electric chair, invented by Harold P Brown, replaces the gallows as the principal method of execution in the United States

• George Eastman introduces the first paper roll-film camera, which he names the 'Kodak'

• Spanish physician Santiago Ramón y Cajal publishes his studies of the central nervous system, which corroborate the neuron theory and lay the foundations of modern neuroscience

• The first modern bra comes on the market, courtesy of Parisian seamstress and shopkeeper Hermione Cadolle

• German physiologist Adolf Eugen Fick manufactures and fits the first successful contact lens

▼ Out and about on a busy Thames in Victorian London, in an 1876 painting, *The Thames*, by James Tissot

Index

Page numbers in *italics* refer to captions.

Picture credits

ABBREVIATIONS: t = top, c = centre, b = bottom, l = left, r = right

Front cover: main image Cyclops Steel Works, Sheffield, in a lithograph by John Rutherford, 1845. **Inset**: an early telephone installed at Osborne House by Queen Victoria in 1878, Cosmos/SSPL/Science Museum, London. **Spine**: early incandescent electric lamp, The Bridgeman Art Library/Science Museum, London. **Back cover**: dress worn by Queen Victoria, Cosmos/SSPL/Science Museum, London. **Page** 2, left to right, top row: Cosmos/SSPL/ Science Museum, London; Corbis/Swim Ink 2, LLC; RMN/Jean-Pierre Lagiewski/musée de la Voiture, Compiègne; 2nd row: Cosmos/SSPL/ Science Museum, London; The Bridgeman Art Library/National Football Museum, Preston; Corbis/Swim Ink 2, LLC, 'La Végétaline' poster by H Mariels, 1921, DR; 3rd row (all 3 images): Cosmos/SSPL/Science Museum, London; bottom row: © with the kind permission of Levi Strauss & Co Archives, San Francisco; The Bridgeman Art Library/Science Museum, London; The Bridgeman Art Library/Museum of London. **Pages** 4/5: Suez Canal © Guido Alberto Rossi/ www.photolibrary.com; 6/7t: Illustration of Neanderthal Man/www.gregcirade.com; 6l & r: Cosmos/SSPL/Science Museum, London; 7tr: Corbis/Rémi Benali; 7bl: AKG-Images, Wolfgang Staudte, 1951; 8tl: The Bridgeman Art Library/Peter Newark Military Pictures, private collection; 8tr: The Bridgeman Art Library/The Stapleton Collection, photo Julia Margaret, 1815-1879; 8b: Leemage/Heritage Images, National Motor Museum, Knight; 9l : The Art Archive/Eileen Tweedy; 9t: Leemage/Costa; 9br: AKG-Images; 10t: AKG-Images/collection Archiv für Kunst & Geschichte, Berlin; 10bl: The Bridgeman Art Library, 'Football' by John Rogers, 1891 © Collection of the New York Historical Society; 10br: Cosmos/SPL/Custom Medical Stock Photo; 11tl: Leemage/Bianchetti; 11tr: Cosmos/SPL/ Mehau Kulyk; 11br: Leemage/Heritage Images/ Oxford Science Archive; 12/13t: AKG-Images/ B Garrett collection; 12bl: AKG-Images/Science Photo Library; 12br & 13bl: Cosmos/SSPL/Science Museum, London; 13tr: Corbis/Zefa/Frithjof Hirdes; 13br: Corbis/Swim Ink 2, LLC, 'La Végétaline', H Mariels, 1921, DR; 14tl: Corbis/Underwood & Underwood/Bettmann collection; 14tr: The Bridgeman Art Library, Bode Museum, Berlin; 14/15ht: Leemage/Photo Josse, musée Carnavalet, Paris; 14b: Cosmos/SSPL/Science Museum, London; 15br: AKG-Images/Science Photo Library/drawing by Ernst Haeckel, 1891; 15bl: Cosmos/SSPL/Science Museum, London; 16t: Leemage/Aisa; 16bl: Leemage/Costa; 16br: Cosmos/SSPL/Science Museum, London; 17tl: RMN/René-Gabriel Ojeda/musée de la Voiture, Compiègne; 17tr: The Bridgeman Art Library/ Museum of London; 17b: Hemis.FR/Axiom; 18/19: Leemage/Photo Josse, painting by Georges Roux, 1889/musée Carnavalet, Paris; 20tr: Leemage/ Heritage Images/Oxford Science Archive; 20b & 21cl: Leemage/Costa; 21cr & 22tr: Cosmos/SSPL/ Science Museum, London; 22l: Leemage/North Wind Pictures; 22/23: Cosmos/SSPL/NRM-Pictorial Collection; 26t: Corbis/J S Johnston; 24b: Leemage/Costa, painting by Marcello Nizzoli, 1898, private collection; 25t: Leemage/Costa; 25b: Cosmos/SPL/Rosenfeld Images Ltd; 26tr: The Picture Desk/The Art Archive/Alfredo Dagli Orti Museo di Antropologia Etnografia, Turin; 26bl: The Picture Desk/The Art Archive/Alfredo Dagli Orti/Rheinischeslandesmuseum, Bonn; 27cr: Leemage/Fototeca; 27t: Illustration of Neanderthal Man/www.gregcirade.com; 28: Cosmos/SSPL/ Science Museum, London; 29cl: The Bridgeman Art Library, private collection; 29tr: Corbis/Mark Bolton; 29br: The Bridgeman Art Library/Archives Charmet/Bibliothèque des Arts décoratifs, Paris; 30t & bl: Cosmos/SSPL/Science Museum, London; 31t: Corbis/Swim Ink 2, LLC; 31b: AKG-Images, from a film by Wolfgang Staudte, 1951; 32t Cosmos/SSPL/Science Museum, London; 32b: Corbis/Bettmann; 33t: Corbis/Rémi Benali; 33b: Corbis/Léonard de Selva; 34: Corbis/Bettmann; 35t: AKG-Images; 35b: RMN/Jean-Pierre Lagiewski/musée de la Voiture, Compiègne; 36c: Corbis; 36tr: Eyedea/Hoa-Qui/Gérald Morand-Grahame; 36b: Corbis/Bill Ross; 37: Corbis/Lester Lefkowitz; 38t: The Bridgeman Art Library/The Natural History Museum, London; 38b: AKG-Images/Erich Lessing; 39t: AKG-Images/Science Photo Library; 39b: Corbis/Martin Harvey; 40/41: Corbis/Frans Lanting; 41t: The Natural History Museum, London; 41b: AKG-Images/Science Photo Library; 42t: The Bridgeman Art Library/ Archives Charmet/Benjamin Rabier, 1901, © Adagp, Paris 2010; 42b: Corbis/René Mattes; 43c: Leemage/Infatti; 43t: Leemage/Fototeca Schéma: Henry Fairfield Osborn, 1927; 44t: The Bridgeman Art Library/The Stapleton Collection, photograph by Julia Margaret 1815-1879; 44b: Corbis/Bettmann; 45: AKG-Images; 46t: Cosmos/ SPL; 46b: The Bridgeman Art Library/'The Warrior' by William McConnell, 1850-1890, William Drummond, London; 47: The Bridgeman Art Library/Peter Newark Military Pictures, private collection; 48l: AKG-Images; 48tr: Leemage/ Selva/'Battleship Potemkin', Sergei Eisenstein, 1925; 49bl: AKG-Images/painting by Montague Dawson, 1895-1973 © By courtesy of Félix Rosenstiel's Widow & Sons Ltd, London, on behalf of the Estate of Montague Dawson; 49r: Corbis/ Bettmann/Jeff Hilton; 50: Cosmos/SSPL/Science Museum, London; 51t: The Art Archive/Gianni Dagli Orti/Musée national de la voiture et du tourisme, Compiègne; 51b: Cosmos/SPL/Sheila Terry; 52t: Leemage/Heritage Images/National Motor Museum, Knight; 52b: Cosmos/SSPL/ Science Museum, London; 53b: Corbis/Schlegel-milch; 53cl: Leemage/Selva, private collection; 53tr: Roger-Viollet/Ullstein Bild; 54t: AKG-Images/ Science Photo Library; 54br: © Renault Commun-ication/Agence Makheia Adolfo Fiori; 54bl: Leemage/Costa; 55tr: Rea/HH/Evelyn Jacq; 55c: AKG-Images; 55br: © Citroën Communication; 54/55b: Leemage/Bianchetti/ 'Modern Times', Charlie Chaplin, 1936; 56t: The Art Archive/Eileen Tweedy; 56c&b: Cosmos/SSPL/Science Museum, London; 57t: AKG-Images; 57b: Leemage/Heritage Images; 58t: AKG-Images/Collection Archiv für Kunst & Geschichte, Berlin; 58b: AKG-Images/ North Wind Picture Archives; 59t Corbis/Henri Bureau; 59b: Cosmos/SSPL/Science Museum, London; 60t: AKG-Images; 60bl: The Art Archive/ Eileen Tweedy/Olive Mount cutting by Thomas Talbot Bury, 1831; 61t: AKG-Images/Erich Lessing/ 'Le Pont de l'Europe', painting by Claude Monet, 1877, Musée Marmottan, Paris; 61b: The Bridgeman Art Library/P B Whitehouse Collection; 62t: Cosmos/SSPL/Science Museum, London; 62b: Leemage/Costa; 63t: AKG-Images; 63b: Corbis/ Construction Photography; 64tr: Leemage/Selva; 64tr: The Bridgeman Art Library/drawing by Jan van Grevenbroeck, 1731-1807, Museo Correr, Venice; 64b: The Bridgeman Art Library/National Football Museum, Preston; 65t: Leemage/Selva/ 'A Football Match', after an engraving by W H Overend, 1890; 65b: The Bridgeman Art Library/'Football' by John Rogers, 1891/ © Collection of the New York Historical Society; 66c: The Bridgeman Art Library National Football Museum, Preston; 66t: Corbis/Oscar White; 67b: Corbis/Liewig Media Sports/Christian Liewig; 68l: Cosmos/SPL/Custom Medical Stock Photo; 68r: Cosmos/SSPL/Science Museum, London; 69t: Eyedea/Keystone/Keystone France; 69b: Corbis/H Amstrong Roberts; 70t: Leemage/Selva/Musée Pasteur, Paris; 70b: Leemage/Selva; 71r: Eyedea/ Rapho/Hervé Gloaguen; 71bl: Leemage/North Wind Pictures; 72tl: The Bridgeman Art Library, private collection; 72tr: Corbis/Bettmann; 73t: Leemage/Bianchetti; 73b: Leemage, private collection; 74t: Eyedea/Keystone/Keystone France; 74r: Leemage/North Wind Pictures; 75t: The Bridgeman Art Library/Hudson River Subway Train, Edwin Levick, 1901/The Stapleton Collection; 75b: The Bridgeman Art Library/ Archives Charmet/Bibliothèque historique de la Ville de Paris, Paris; 76t: AKG-Images/Entrance to Friedrichstrasse station, watercolour by Fritz Beckert, 1913/Collection Archiv für Kunst & Geschichte, Berlin, DR; 76b: Eyedea/Top/Jarry-Tripelon Sculpture Honsell-Weiss, DR; 77b: Corbis/Roger Ressmeyer; 77tr: Cosmos/SPL/ Mehau Kulyk; 78t: Corbis/NASA; 78c: AKG-Images/B Garrett collection; 78b: AKG-Images; 79b: Corbis/Danny Lehman; 80cl: The Bridgeman Art Library/with kind permission of the University of Edinburgh, Edinburgh University Library; 80br: AKG-Images/Science Photo Library; 81t: Corbis/ Art Becker Photography/Art Becker; 81c: Cosmos/ SSPL/Science Museum, London; 82c: BSIP/ Ablestock; 82t: Corbis/Bettmann; 83t: The Bridgeman Art Library/'El bano', painting by Leopoldo García Ramón, 1902/Museo de San Pio V, Valencia/© AISA/DR; 83b: Corbis/Tim Pannell; 845: Leemage/Heritage Images/Oxford Science Archive; 84b: Cosmos/SPL/Kaj R Svensson; 85t: Corbis/Zefa/Frithjof Hirdes; 85b: Corbis/Swim Ink 2, LLC, 'La Végétaline' poster by H Mariels, 1921, DR; 86c & t: Cosmos/SSPL/Science Museum, London; 86b: Corbis/Bettmann; 87t: Leemage/ Heritage Images/Oxford Science Archive; 87b & 88tr: Cosmos/SSPL/Science Museum, London; 88bl: AKG-Images; 89tr: Cosmos/SSPL/Science Museum, London; 89b: AKG-Images/Ulrich Mattner; 90: Leemage/Photo Josse, Bibliothèque nationale, Paris; 91t: Leemage/Photo Josse, 'Fête de nuit à l'Exposition universelle de 1889 sous la tour Eiffel', painting by Georges Roux, 1889/ Musée Carnavalet, Paris; 91c: AKG-Images/The Machine Hall at the Universal Exposition, Paris, 1889/Collection Archiv für Kunst & Geschichte, Berlin; 91b: Leemage/Selva; 92tl: Corbis/ Bettmann; 92b: Leemage/Photo Josse, Musée Carnavalet, Paris; 93t: SRD/Jean-Pierre Delagarde; 93c: Corbis/Swim Ink 2, LLC, Chicago 1934, Sandor DR; 94br: AKG-Images/Electa, Fauteuil Barcelona, 1929, chair by Ludwig Mies van der Rohe/© Adagp, Paris 2010; 94b: Corbis/ Arcaid/David Clapp/architect Ludwig Mies van der Rohe/© Adagp, Paris 2010; 95tl: AKG-Images/ Ullstein Bild; 95r: Corbis/Ron Watts, Space Needle, 1962, architect John Graham DR; 96tr: AKG-Images/drawing by Aloys Eckhardt, 1845-1906; 96cl: The Picture Desk/Dagli Orti Collection/Culver Pictures; 97t: Cosmos/SSPL/Science Museum, London; 97b: Corbis/Underwood & Underwood/ Bettmann collection; 98tr: Cosmos/SSPL/Science Museum, London; 98b: Corbis/Hulton-Deutsch Collection; 99t: REA/Jean-Claude Moschetti; 99b: Corbis/ Photo Cuisine collection; 100t: AKG-Images; 100b: AKG-Images/Remington, 1910, Léonetto Cappiello/© Adagp, Paris 2010; 101t: Corbis/Layne Kennedy; 101b: Cosmos/SSPL/ Science Museum, London; 102t: Corbis/ Underwood & Underwood/Bettmann collection; 102b: The Bridgeman Art Library, Victorian secretary and her typing maching, Peter Jackson, 1922-2003/© Look and Learn, private collection; 103t: Cosmos/SSPL/Science Museum, London; 103b: Corbis/Underwood & Underwood/Bettmann collection; 104t: AKG-Images/National Archaeological Museum, Athens; 104b & 105c: AKG-Images; 105br: The Bridgeman Art Library/Bode Museum, Berlin; 106tl: Corbis/ Bureau/Troy, Wolfgang Petersen 2004/LA Collection, Warner Brothers, Alex Bailey; 106c: The Bridgeman Art Library/Ashmolean Museum, University of Oxford; 106b: AKG-Images/Peter Connolly; 107t: AKG-Images, photograph Delie & Bechard, 1878/B Garrett collection; 107b: © CNRS Photothèque/LC2RMF, Alexis Chezière; 108t: Corbis/Bruce Burkhardt; 108bl: Rue des Archives/RDA, Marlon Brando in 'The Wild One' directed by Laszlo Benedek, 1954; 108br: © with kind permission of Levi Strauss & Co Archives, San Francisco; 109tc: Corbis/Visuals Unlimited; 109tr: Corbis/Encyclopedia collection; 110tl: Cosmos/SSPL/Science Museum, London; 110c: The Bridgeman Art Library/Archives Charmet, from 'Manuel d'anatomie descriptive du corps humain' by Jules Cloquet/Musée d'Histoire de la Médecine, Paris; 110b: AKG-Images/Science Photo Library/drawing by Ernst Haeckel, 1891; 111t: BSIP/David M Phillips; 111b: Cosmos/SPL/ Dr G Moscoso; 112tr: AKG-Images/Science Photo Library; 112l: Leemage/Bianchetti; 113t: AKG-Images; 113br: Cosmos/SSPL/Science Museum, London; 114: The Art Archive/Culver Pictures; 115tc: Cosmos/SSPL/Science Museum, London; 115l: Christophel Collection; 115tr: Leemage/ United Archives; 116t & c: Leemage/Bianchetti; 116b: The Art Archive/Culver Pictures; 117: AFP/Antonio Scorza; 118t: The Bridgeman Art Library/Archives Charmet/private collection; 118b: Cosmos/SPL/Library of Congress, Washington DC; 119t: AKG-Images; 119b: Corbis/Waldon Fawcett; 120t: Leemage/Heritage Images; 120bl: Cosmos/ SSPL/Science Museum, London; 121t: © BPK, Berlin, Dist RMN/Martin Franken/Ethnological Museum, Berlin; 121b: Cosmos/SSPL/Science Museum, London; 122t: AKG-Images; 122b: Leemage/Costa; 123t: The Art Archive/Culver Pictures; 123c: © Deutsche Grammophon/A Universal Music Company; 123b: Leemage/ Gusman; 124: René Jacques/© Ministère de la Culture, Médiathèque du Patrimoine, Paris, Dist. RMN, photograph by René-Jacques of his sister, 1927; 125tl: Leemage/Gusman; 125tr: Corbis/ Amanaimages/Kaoru Mikami; 125cr: Corbis/Guido Cozzi; 125b: © Apple; 126tl: Leemage/Heritage Images/Oxford Science Archive; 126tr: The Bridgeman Art Library/Science Museum, London; 127: Grégoire Cirade; 128t: Leemage/Aisa; 128b: Corbis/Michael Freeman; 129t: Corbis/ Schenectady Museum, Hall of Electrical History Foundation, New York; 129b: AKG-Images; 130c: Cosmos/SSPL/Science Museum, London; 130t: Corbis/John Springer Collection; 131bl: Corbis/ Kurt Stier; 131br: Leemage/Selva/private collection; 132t: Roger-Viollet/Alinari; 132b: The Bridgeman Art Library/lithograph by Henry Alken, 1819, private collection; 133t: RMN/René-Gabriel Ojeda/musée de la Voiture, Compiègne; 133b: Roger-Viollet/Maurice Branger; 134: Roger-Viollet/ TopFoto/Ken Russell; 135t: The Bridgeman Art Library/Archives Charmet/Conservatoire national des Arts et Métiers, Paris; 135b: The Picture Desk/The Art Archive/Gianni Dagli Orti/'The Rover' poster by G Moore, musée d'Art et d'Industrie, Saint-Étienne; 136t: AKG-Images/Ullstein Bild; 136cl: Kharbine-Tapabor/Galdoc-Grob collection/ Michelin poster by Fabian Fabiano, 1910; 136cr: AKG-Images; 137t: Corbis/TempSport/Jérôme Prévost; 137b: Corbis/Roger Ressmeyer; 138: Cosmos/SPL/Maximilian Stock Ltd; 139t: The Bridgeman Art Library/Museum of London; 139b: REA/Ludovic; 140l: The Bridgeman Art Library/ Unloading tea at London Docks, engraving by William Bazett Murray/The Stapleton Collection; 140br: Corbis/Hulton-Deutsch Collection; 141t: Leemage/Aisa, painting by Claude Monet, 1904/musée d'Orsay, Paris; 141b: Leemage/ Heritage Images, Lloyd's of London, engraving by William Bazett Murray, 1877; 142t: The Bridgeman Art Library, Royal London Exchange, Harley Crossley, private collection; 142b: Hemis.FR/Axiom; 143t : The Bridgeman Art Library, 'The Thames', painting by Jacques James Joseph Tissot, 1876, Wakefield Museums and Galleries, West Yorkshire; 143br: Corbis/Free Agents Limited; 144/145: The Art Archive/Culver Pictures; 146tr: The Picture Desk/The Art Archive/Alfredo Dagli Orti/ Rheinischeslandesmuseum, Bonn; 146bl: Cosmos/ SSPL/Science Museum, London; 146br: Leemage/ Photo Josse, Bibliothèque nationale, Paris; 147t: Corbis/Swim Ink 2, LLC; 147bl: Cosmos/SSPL/ Science Museum, London; 147br: The Bridgeman Art Library/'The Warrior' by William McConnell 1850-1890/William Drummond, London; 148tl: AKG-Images/Science Photo Library; 148bl: Cosmos/SSPL/Science Museum, London; 148br: Corbis/Bettmann; 149tr: The Bridgeman Art Library/with kind permission of Edinburgh University Library, Edinburgh University; 149b: The Bridgeman Art Library/National Football Museum, Preston; 149br: Corbis/Bettmann; 150t: Corbis/NASA; 150bl: Cosmos/SSPL/Science Museum, London; 150br: AKG-Images/National Archaeological Museum, Athens; 151t: © with kind permission of Levi Strauss & Co Archives, San Francisco; 151bl: AKG-Images; 151br: The Bridgeman Art Library/Archives Charmet, private collection; 152cl: Leemage/Selva; 152bl: Cosmos/ SSPL/Science Museum, London; 152br: Roger-Viollet/TopFoto/Ken Russell; 153t: Cosmos/SPL/ Maximilian Stock Ltd; 153bl: Cosmos/SSPL/ Science Museum, London; 153br: The Bridgeman Art Library/'The Thames', painting by Jacques James Joseph Tissot, 1876/Wakefield Museums and Galleries, West Yorkshire.

Illustration of the internal combustion engine on page 54 by Grégoire Cirade.

THE ADVENTURE OF DISCOVERIES AND INVENTIONS
The Railway Age – 1855 to 1880
Published in 2010 in the United Kingdom by Vivat Direct Limited
(t/a Reader's Digest), 157 Edgware Road, London W2 2HR

The Railway Age – 1855 to 1880 is owned and under licence from
The Reader's Digest Association, Inc. All rights reserved.

Adapted from *L'Ère de la Motorisation*, part of a series entitled L'ÉPOPÉE DES
DÉCOUVERTES ET DES INVENTIONS, created in France by BOOKMAKER and
first published by Sélection du Reader's Digest, Paris, in 2010.

Translated from French by Peter Lewis

PROJECT TEAM
Series editor Christine Noble
Art editor Julie Bennett
Designer Martin Bennett
Consultant Ruth Binney
Proofreader Ron Pankhurst
Indexer Marie Lorimer

Colour origination FMG
Printed and bound in Europe by Arvato Iberia

FOR VIVAT DIRECT
Editorial director Julian Browne
Art director Anne-Marie Bulat
Managing editor Nina Hathway
Picture resource manager Sarah Stewart-Richardson
Prepress technical manager Dean Russell
Product production manager Claudette Bramble
Production controller Sandra Fuller

We are committed to both the quality of our products and the service we provide to our
customers. We value your comments, so please feel free to contact us on 08705 113366
or via our website at **www.readersdigest.co.uk**

If you have any comments or suggestions about the content of our books, you can
email us at **gbeditorial@readersdigest.co.uk**

CONCEPT CODE: FR0104/IC/S
BOOK CODE: 642-007 UP0000-1
ISBN: 978-0-276-44519-4
ORACLE CODE: 356400007H.00.24